The Climate Crisis

ISSUES

Volume 95

Editor

Craig Donnellan

Educational Publishers
Cambridge

First published by Independence
PO Box 295
Cambridge CB1 3XP
England

British Library Cataloguing in Publication Data
The Climate Crisis – (Issues Series)
I. Donnellan, Craig II. Series
363.7'3874

ISBN 1 86168 303 0

Printed in Great Britain
MWL Print Group Ltd

Typeset by
Claire Boyd

Cover
The illustration on the front cover is by
Pumpkin House.

CONTENTS

Chapter One: Climate Change

Chapter Two: The Effects

Chapter Three: Solutions

Introduction

The Climate Crisis is the ninety-fifth volume in the **Issues** series. The aim of this series is to offer up-to-date information about important issues in our world.

The Climate Crisis looks at global warming and climate change effects and solutions.

The information comes from a wide variety of sources and includes:
Government reports and statistics
Newspaper reports and features
Magazine articles and surveys
Website material
Literature from lobby groups
and charitable organisations.

It is hoped that, as you read about the many aspects of the issues explored in this book, you will critically evaluate the information presented. It is important that you decide whether you are being presented with facts or opinions. Does the writer give a biased or an unbiased report? If an opinion is being expressed, do you agree with the writer?

The Climate Crisis offers a useful starting-point for those who need convenient access to information about the many issues involved. However, it is only a starting-point. At the back of the book is a list of organisations which you may want to contact for further information.

*****

Background information on climate change

The threat of climate change

Climate change is likely to have a significant impact on the global environment. In general, the faster the climate changes, the greater will be the risk of damage. Mean sea level is expected to rise 15-95 cm by the year 2100, causing flooding of low-lying areas and other damage. Climatic zones could shift towards the poles by 150-550 km in the mid-latitude regions. Forests, deserts, rangelands and other unmanaged ecosystems would face new climatic stresses. As a result, many will decline or fragment, and individual species will become extinct.

Human society will face new risk and pressures. Food security is unlikely to be threatened at the global level, but some regions are likely to experience food shortages and hunger. Water resources will be affected as precipitation and evaporation patterns change around the world. Physical infrastructure will be damaged, particularly by sea-level rise and by extreme weather events. Economic activities, human settlements, and human health will experience many direct and indirect effects. The poor and disadvantaged are the most vulnerable to the negative consequences of climate change.

Understanding climate change:

The greenhouse effect

The earth's climate is driven by a continuous flow of energy from the sun. This energy arrives mainly in the form of visible light. About 30% is immediately scattered back into space, but most of the 70% that is absorbed passes down through the atmosphere to warm the earth's surface. (Without this natural greenhouse effect the earth would be

about 30 degrees Celsius cooler and would be unfit for us to live on!) The earth must send this energy back into space in the form of infrared radiation. Being much cooler than the sun, the earth does not emit energy as visible light. Instead, it emits infrared, or thermal radiation.

'Greenhouse gases' in the atmosphere block infrared radiation from escaping directly from the surface to space. Infrared radiation cannot pass straight through the air like visible light. Instead, most departing energy is carried away from the surface by air currents and clouds, eventually escaping to space from altitudes above the thickest layers of the greenhouse gas blanket.

The main greenhouse gases are water vapour, carbon dioxide, ozone, methane, nitrous oxide, and the chlorfluorcarbons (CFCs). Levels of all key greenhouse gases (with the possible exception of water vapour) are rising as a direct result of human activity. Emissions of carbon dioxide (mainly from burning coal, oil, and natural gas), methane and nitrous oxide (due to agriculture and changes in land use), ozone (generated by chemical reactions to the fumes in car exhausts) and CFCs (manufactured by industry) are changing how the atmosphere absorbs energy. This is all happening at an unprecedented speed. The result is known as the 'enhanced greenhouse effect'.

The climate system must adjust to rising greenhouse gas levels to keep the global 'energy budget' in balance. In the long term, the earth must get rid of energy at the same rate at which it receives energy from the sun. Since a thicker blanket of greenhouse gases helps to reduce energy loss to space, the climate must change somehow to restore the balance between incoming and outgoing energy. This adjustment will include a 'global warming' of the earth's surface and lower atmosphere. But this is only part of the story. Warming up is the simplest way for the climate to get rid of the extra energy. But even small rise in temperature will be accompanied by many other changes: in cloud cover and wind patterns, for example. Some of these changes may act to enhance the warming, others to counteract it.

■ The above information is from Climate Action Network Europe's website which can be found at www.climnet.org

© Climate Action Network Europe

Climate change

Information from United Utilities

The average temperature of the atmosphere has always been changing. It has been on a warming phase for decades, but it is thought that this may be happening too quickly for natural and human communities to deal with. One of the chief causes of this rapid rate of change is an increase in global warming, caused by the growth in the burning of fossil fuels to satisfy ever-growing demand for energy.

Why is our climate changing?

Most of the energy available on Earth comes from the Sun. It arrives as radiation (heat, light, radio-waves). In just one second the Earth receives more energy than all the electricity used in the UK in a whole month! All the energy received from the sun is eventually converted (transformed) into heat and re-radiated out into space, i. e. the energy that arrives as light leaves as heat.

The carbon dioxide in the atmosphere absorbs and thus helps retain heat from the Sun. The higher the concentration of CO_2 the longer heat is retained before it is lost to space, and in turn, the warmer the atmosphere becomes.

This is similar to what happens in a greenhouse. The glass lets sunlight in but absorbs the outgoing heat, warming up the entire greenhouse. Hence the name *greenhouse effect* to describe the way carbon dioxide and other gases affect global temperatures.

If there were no carbon dioxide in our atmosphere, then the average surface temperature of the Earth would be MINUS 15°C or lower. Life as we know it would not exist. Even with the present level of only about 0.04% carbon dioxide (one molecule of CO_2 in every 2, 500 of air) it holds enough heat to keep the average at about PLUS 15°C. The amount of carbon dioxide in the atmosphere is the result of four main processes.

i.   The amount of carbon dioxide absorbed by plants (photo-synthesis).

ii. The amount of carbon dioxide released by fires and living things (combustion and respiration).

iii. The amount of carbon dioxide released by volcanic activity.

iv. The amount being converted into fossil fuels (and trapped below ground as coal, oil and natural gas) rather than being respired or burnt.

Each geological period has its own balance between these processes and hence its own carbon dioxide concentration, global temperature regime and climate pattern.

Carbon dioxide is now being added to the atmosphere faster than it is being absorbed. The prime source is the burning of fossil fuels, such as at power stations to generate electricity. The rate of their use has risen many times since the start of the Industrial Revolution and is still increasing.

Tropical rainforests are amongst the best eco-systems to absorb and retain this excess of CO_2. Unfortunately, many are being felled for timber or to make way for farms. Because felling destroys both these forest communities and the soil that supported them, natural regeneration of tropical rainforest is at best slow, and sometimes impossible.

The seas also dissolve CO_2, so far taking up about half that produced by industrialisation. How much more can be absorbed is not known, especially as the seas' temperatures rise as they absorb heat from the atmosphere.

What is the potential impact of global warming?

Global warming and climate change demonstrate the impact of industrialisation and energy-demanding life-

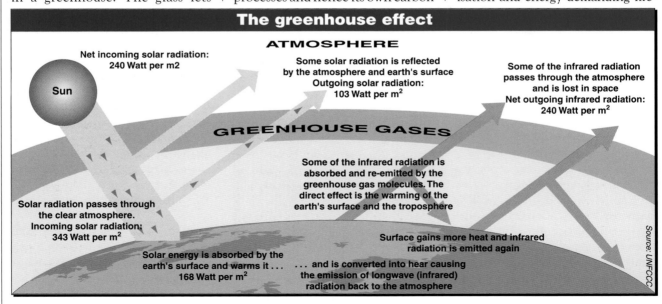

The greenhouse effect

ATMOSPHERE

Net incoming solar radiation: 240 Watt per m2

Sun

Some solar radiation is reflected by the atmosphere and earth's surface
Outgoing solar radiation: 103 Watt per m²

Some of the infrared radiation passes through the atmosphere and is lost in space
Net outgoing infrared radiation: 240 Watt per m²

GREENHOUSE GASES

Some of the infrared radiation is absorbed and re-emitted by the greenhouse gas molecules. The direct effect is the warming of the earth's surface and the troposphere

Solar radiation passes through the clear atmosphere.
Incoming solar radiation: 343 Watt per m²

Solar energy is absorbed by the earth's surface and warms it . . .
168 Watt per m²

. . . and is converted into hear causing the emission of longwave (infrared) radiation back to the atmosphere

Surface gains more heat and infrared radiation is emitted again

Source: UNFCCC

styles on the whole world and raise many social, ethical and political issues in addition to the scientific and geographical facts and possible technological remedies. Global warming is likely to result in:

- An increase in the severity and frequency of storms leading to damage to crops, buildings and more coastal erosion.
- Rainfall, leading to new areas being subject to flooding, affecting
  – farming and forestry through water-logging of soils and the erosion of fertile top-soil,
  – fresh-water fisheries through loss of plants and erosion of stream beds,
  – off-shore fisheries through deposition of silt,
  – the effectiveness of sewage treatment, through overloading the processing works,
  – homes and towns.
- A change in the global distribution of areas subject to drought, affecting
  – farming, forestry and fisheries
  – the availability of drinking water
  – the generation of electricity from conventional power stations through an inadequate supply of cooling water.
- An increase in the incidence of tropical pests and diseases in previously temperate regions.
- Difficulty for many plants and animals in adapting quickly enough to their rapidly changing environments.
- Warming of the oceans so that they expand, flooding low-lying coastal areas, including some of the most productive agricultural land on the planet and many of its larger cities.
- Land-based glaciers and ice-fields melting faster than new snow is being added, so raising sea-level further, threatening additional coastal areas with inundation.
- Disruption in water supply, health and transport systems.

A most alarming feature of all these impacts is that taken together they could trigger conflict between communities and nations as they struggle to cope with the changes in their environments and lifestyles.

Averages may not tell the whole story

Though the average global temperature may rise, this single figure may not tell the whole story. For example, it does not mean that they will go up everywhere or for the whole year. As a result of global warming, the UK may actually become colder!

At present, the Gulf Stream flows from the seas of the West Indies, across the northern Atlantic and bathes the west coast of the UK. This warms the weather systems that approach from the west and gives the UK relatively mild winters.

Two things could disrupt the flow of the Gulf Stream.
i. An increase in the ocean temperature, reducing its density.
ii. An increase in the volume of fresh-water flowing into the Arctic and northern Atlantic Oceans reducing their salinity.

Together these might be enough to cause the Gulf Stream to take a more southerly course, or stop altogether. Then the UK would be exposed to winters as severe as other lands at the same latitude, such as Alaska and Siberia. Some scientists think this change might take centuries, but others are of the opinion it could take as little as two decades!

So what can we do to offset the potential harm caused by global warming?

Global warming over the last 100 years or so is now well established. The causes seem to be a combination of both natural warming after the so-called Little Ice Age (ca. 1650-1900) and the impact of industrialisation. Explanations of the past, and predictions about the future, are based on mathematical models run on computers. It will be many years before anybody can be sure which model accurately describes the flow of energy through land, air and sea and how this affects weather, climate, ocean currents, etc.

If we wait until then before doing anything, it could be too late. Action now has to be based on best guesses of what is true and the magnitude of the potential disruption to human health, wealth and happiness that could result from doing nothing. This approach is known as the Precautionary Principle.

Everyone should take action now to reduce their emissions of carbon dioxide through more efficient use of energy, the use of renewable and alternative forms of energy, and through the planting of trees to absorb at least some of the carbon dioxide that they do release.

Schools, as educators of future energy consumers, should take a lead role in raising awareness of the issues and demonstrating best practice in energy management to reduce CO_2 emissions. The activities on our website seek to help schools achieve this task.

Misconceptions

There are two common misunderstandings about climate change and its effects

- The ozone hole is the cause of global warming.

The ozone in the high atmosphere absorbs ultra-violet light and thus protects animals and plants from the damage that these rays can cause. Reductions in the concentration of ozone in the stratosphere are caused by several types of chemicals. The most notorious are the chloro-fluoro-carbon compounds (CFCs) once used in fridges, blown foam and as aerosol propellants. CFCs and ozone have no direct effect on global warming because they have no significant effect on the visible light and heat radiation that influences the Earth's temperature regime.

- The melting of the Arctic ice sheet raises sea-level.

This is not true because it is already floating on the Arctic Ocean. (Think of Archimedes' Principle.) It is only the melting of ice that is resting above sea-level on solid ground that affects sea-level. The main ice-fields involved are in Antarctica, the Himalayas, the Alps, the Rockies, the Andes and Greenland.

■ The above information is from United Utilities. For further information visit their website at www.unitedutilities.com

Global warming

Introduction

Global warming is the increase of average world temperatures as a result of what is known as the greenhouse effect. Certain gases in the atmosphere act like glass in a greenhouse, allowing sunlight through to heat the Earth's surface but trapping the heat as it radiates back into space. As the greenhouse gases build up in the atmosphere the Earth gets hotter.

Causes

One of the main greenhouse gases is carbon dioxide (CO_2). As trees grow they take in CO_2 from the air. When the wood dies the CO_2 is returned to the air. Forest clearance and wood burning (such as happens in tropical rain forests) is increasing the latter half of the process, adding to the CO_2 in the atmosphere. Deforestation is now out of control. For example in 1987 an area of the Amazon rain forest the size of Britain was burned, adding 500 million tonnes of CO_2 to the atmosphere. The loss of the forests also means that there are fewer trees to absorb CO_2.

The recent fires in Indonesia, with more than a million hectares of forest ablaze, thanks to fires set deliberately by logging companies, are likely to have an effect on global climate, but the more immediate effect has been the cloud of smog which enveloped much of south-east Asia during September and early October 1997.

However, as large a contribution as deforestation makes , it causes less than half the yearly total of CO_2, the rest comes from the burning of coal, oil and other fossil fuels. These fossil fuels are burned in cars, power stations and factories of the wealthier nations such as the USA, Western Europe and the USSR.

Televisions, lights and computers use electricity that is created mainly from burning coal. Every time we switch on a light we are adding to the greenhouse effect. Cars are also

major sources of CO_2. The average European is responsible for nearly 2.5 times as much atmospheric carbon as a Latin American. The concentration of CO_2 has increased 25% since the industrial revolution, half of this rise has been in the last 30 years. It is expected to double within decades.

Other greenhouse gases

CO_2 contributes about 50% to the greenhouse effect. The other greenhouse gases are methane, chlorofluorocarbons (CFCs) and nitrous oxide (N_2O)

Methane – is released during coal-mining activities, oil exploration and when vegetation is burnt during land clearance. The main source of methane though is agricultural activity. It is released from wetlands such as rice paddies and from animals, particularly cud-chewing species like cows. The problem with methane is that as the world population increases, agricultural activity must increase and so emissions of methane will also increase. Since the 1960s the amount of methane in the air has increased by 1% per year – twice as fast as the build up of CO_2.

Nitrous oxide – comes from both natural and man-made processes. Man influenced sources, which represent about 45% of output to the atmosphere, are mainly: fossil fuel combustion, as in power stations; use of nitrogenous fertilisers; burning rain forests and human and animal waste. N_2O contributes about 6% to the greenhouse effect at the moment.

CFCs – found in fridges, air conditioners, aerosols etc. are extremely effective greenhouse gases. Although there are lower concentrations of CFCs in the atmosphere than CO_2 they trap more heat. A CFC molecule is 10,000 times more effective in trapping heat than a CO_2 molecule, methane is about 30 times more effective. Methane molecules survive for 10 years in the atmosphere and CFCs for 110 years. It is this that causes people to want to ban them completely.

POLLUTER!

Feedback process

CO_2 – about half the CO_2 released by burning fossil fuels is absorbed by the oceans. It is taken up by minute sea creatures or dragged to the ocean depths by the circulation of water. Recent research suggests that as the Earth heats up, the oceans will be less efficient in absorbing CO_2, leaving more in the atmosphere and so adding further to global warming.

Methane – as global temperatures become greater, so large quantities of methane stored in the frozen tundra of the north may be released. Also methane trapped in the sea bed may be freed by temperature rises.

As the world warms it causes feedback processes. Increases in temperature cause the liberation of CO_2 and methane which then cause further warming. Another feedback mechanism arises through higher air temperatures evaporating more water and so providing more cloud which both traps heat from below and reflects back sunlight from above. As the world warms, the effect of clouds could become more and more significant.

Effects

If no action is taken the greenhouse effect could lead to a rise in average global temperatures of between 1.5-4.5 degrees Celcius as early as the year 2030. These rises will be greater towards the poles and less at the tropics. There will also be more warming in winter than summer. Such increases will make the world hotter than it has been for more than 100,000 years. The rise will also be faster than ever before; a rise of 3 degrees Celcius after the last ice age took thousands of years. By the end of next century temperatures could have reached those of the time of the dinosaurs and it is doubtful if humans could survive. The effects are already showing – the ten hottest years since the 1860s have been in the last 15 years.

Storms – storms and hurricanes will become more frequent and stronger as oceans heat up causing more water to evaporate. Evidence is building up at an alarming rate. In September 1991 Japan was hit by Typhoon Mireille, its worst for 30

years. Then in September 1993 it was hit by Typhoon Yancy – the 13th that year, and the worst for 50 years. In January 1993 barometric pressure around Shetland dropped to its lowest recorded level, 915 millibars. The oil tanker *Braer* broke up in the resulting storm. In March 1993 the 'Storm of the Century' hit America, causing $1.6 billion in damage from Canada to Cuba. In December 1993 hurricane-force storms caused Britain its worst flooding for 40 years.

Droughts – continental heartlands will dry out more in summer. In 1988 the US suffered its worst heat wave and drought for 50 years. It cannot be proved that this was due to the greenhouse effect but it does give us some idea of what to expect in the future.

Floods – sea levels are already rising at a rate of 1 to 2mm each year due to expansion of the top layer of the oceans as they warm and the melting of the polar ice caps. The predicted rise by 2050 is between 20 and 50cm. This will cause increased flooding in coastal areas and river estuaries such as Bangladesh and the Nile Delta. London and many other British coastal cities will be threatened also. It is now a priority to strengthen Britain's sea defences.

What can be done?

It is important to slow the warming as much as possible. This means using less fossil fuel, eliminating CFCs

---

If no action is taken the greenhouse effect could lead to a rise in average global temperatures of between 1.5-4.5 degrees Celcius as early as the year 2030

---

altogether, and slowing down deforestation.

This can be achieved best through energy conservation, including better use of public transport and cleaner, more efficient cars; and energy efficiency by greater use of gas which produces less CO_2 than coal and oil, and through renewable energy such as solar power. We need to stop destroying rain forests (deforestation) and start replanting trees (afforestation) to soak up carbon dioxide.

A United Nations panel has estimated that we need to reduce global fuel use by 60% immediately in order to stabilise the climate. Current commitments by those governments participating in CO_2 reduction will only lower global CO_2 by 4-6%. Although the developed industrialised nations still produce most CO_2, the rapidly developing nations of South America and Asia are increasing their CO_2 production at a much higher rate, and by 2010 they will overtake the West as the main producers of CO_2.

The developing countries are reluctant to participate in any CO_2 emission reduction plans, arguing that they did not create global warming and that it is the responsibility of developed countries to cut their own emissions or to support developing countries with financial aid. Oil producing countries – including a significant lobby in the US – are also reluctant to have their sales reduced and have protested against action on climate change.

Nuclear power – does not produce CO_2 so could replace other forms of energy. It is necessary though, to find an effective means of safely disposing of the radioactive waste that can remain dangerous for hundreds to thousands of years.

Alternative energy – more funding is required for research and development of alternative pollution-free energy sources such as solar, wave and wind energy.

■ The above information is from the Young People's Trust for the Environment's website which can be found at www.yptenc.org.uk

© Young People's Trust for the Environment

Climate change

Scientific certainties and uncertainties

Climate change is the most important environmental issue we face this century.

Every one of the hottest 15 years on record has occurred since 1980 – the hottest five since 1997.

The natural greenhouse effect

Some gases in our atmosphere, for example carbon dioxide, methane, nitrous oxide, and especially water vapour, trap heat emitted from the Earth's surface, keeping the planet about 30°C warmer than it would otherwise be. This is the 'natural greenhouse effect' and is scientifically well understood.

Human activities, especially the burning of fossil fuels like coal and oil, have increased the level of these greenhouse gases in our atmosphere. This is throwing the climate system out of balance, causing global warming at the surface.

The Earth has experienced major climate variations in the past: ice ages have come and gone many times before. Right now we are in an interglacial, a relatively mild period between ice ages. But human activities are changing the climate system.

Can we distinguish human effects from those caused by nature?

The United Nations Intergovernmental Panel on Climate Change (IPCC) is recognised worldwide as the definitive source of information on climate change. In 1995 it concluded that the balance of evidence suggests a noticeable human influence on global climate and, in a further report in 2001, the IPCC concluded that most of the observed warming over the last 50 years is likely to be attributable to human activities.

Here we look at the scientific certainties and uncertainties about climate change and its impact on the environment.

The information in this article is gathered from a wide range of published international sources. It includes work by scientists funded by the Met Office, the Natural Environment Research Council, and the Department of the Environment, Food and Rural Affairs.

Widely accepted facts

■ Carbon dioxide and nitrous oxide levels are rising, primarily as a result of human activities connected with the burning of fossil fuels. Methane levels are rising, though the rise has slowed down recently.

■ The order of importance in contributing to human-induced greenhouse effect is carbon dioxide (60%), methane (20%), nitrous oxide and other gases (20%).

■ Carbon dioxide levels in the atmosphere have increased from about 280ppm (parts per million) in the mid-18th century – the start of the industrial revolution – to around 379ppm today. You would need to go back millions of years to find such high levels of carbon dioxide in the atmosphere. Methane levels in the atmosphere more than doubled in the last century.

■ Nitrous oxide levels are rising by about 0.25% each year.

■ Over the last century average global surface temperature rose by around 0.7°C. Continents in the northern hemisphere have warmed the most.

■ 1998 was the warmest year recorded for the globe since 1860, the earliest year for which a precise global estimate is possible; 2002 and 2003 tie for second place.

■ The majority of the world's mountain glaciers are retreating and Arctic sea-ice appears to be reducing in both extent and thickness.

■ Global sea levels have risen 10-20cm over the past 100 years.

With so many factors to consider how can we predict the climate with any accuracy?

Models of the Earth system, based on sound physical, chemical and biological principles, are the best tools for evaluating what may happen in the future. We can test climate models by looking at how well they reproduce past and current climate. While current models are not perfect, they are improving all the time.

The Natural Environment Research Council fund the world's largest climate change prediction experiment www.climateprediction.net. The experiment will allow us to carry out thousands of predictions with slightly modified versions of the model and so more thoroughly investigate the range of uncertainty.

UK scientists are developing and testing state-of-the-art climate models, for example, the HiGEM project (www.higem.nerc.ac.uk), which will develop one of the world's highest resolution global Earth system models. The UK and Japan are collaborating on a project that will run this high-resolution model on one of the world's biggest computers (www.earthsimulator.org.uk).

What is likely to happen?
Global consequences
The IPCC has developed a number of future emissions scenarios, explored by a range of climate models. They show that:

■ Carbon dioxide levels are likely to at least double from pre-industrial levels by the end of this century. When other factors are added, such as increased water vapour, the estimated average global temperature rise by 2100 is between 1·5-5.8°C.

■ This rate of warming is much larger than experienced during the 20th century and is very likely to be unprecedented in the last 10,000 years.

■ Global sea level is likely to rise by 10-90cm over this century. Low-lying coasts will flood, affecting many human settlements, including some major cities, and some habitats will be lost.

- If temperatures over Greenland increase by more than about 3°C – which appears likely based on current model predictions, the ice sheet there will eventually disappear altogether – raising global sea level by several meters over a period of 1,000 years or more.
- Some regions and seasons will become wetter, others drier. Summer droughts are likely to intensify in the interiors of continents. Tropical cyclones may become more severe. Intense cold weather will become rarer.
- Many areas will experience more extremely hot periods, like the unprecedented heat in Europe in 2003, and heavier rain with an increased risk of flooding.
- Food production in mid-latitudes could benefit if climate change is not too severe. However, in tropical and sub-tropical regions the risk of famine is likely to increase.
- People in regions where water is already scarce, particularly in the sub-tropics, are likely to see water availability decline.
- The world's vegetation zones will undergo major changes, in particular, boundary shifts between grasslands, forests and shrublands.
- Freshwater systems will experience changes in temperature, flows and levels, affecting biodiversity, water supplies and water quality.
- Human and animal diseases, such as malaria, are predicted to spread to new areas and deaths related to heat stress are predicted to increase.
- Large migrations of people away from high flood risk areas or arid regions are predicted to produce 'environmental migrants' which could drive conflicts and increase health problems.

Consequences in the UK
Most of the expected global impacts of climate change will affect the UK, either directly or indirectly. Insurance companies already take the

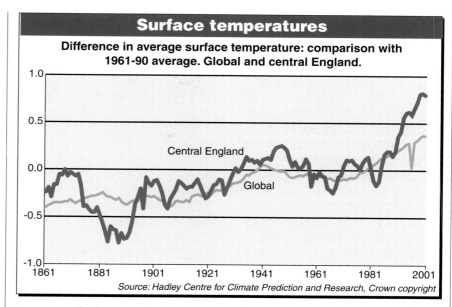

Surface temperatures

Difference in average surface temperature: comparison with 1961-90 average. Global and central England.

Source: Hadley Centre for Climate Prediction and Research, Crown copyright

impacts of climate change very seriously.

By 2080 predictions suggest temperatures may rise 2-3.5°C, winters will become wetter and summers drier, sea levels will rise, extreme sea levels may become more frequent and cloud cover in the south may reduce increasing the risk of skin cancer.

More heatwaves are predicted with an increase in heat-related deaths to around 2,800 cases per year. This is likely to be offset by fewer cold related deaths.

Flooding and landslides are predicted to become more frequent disrupting road and rail networks. Warmer water fish such as mullet, bass, sole and bream are already replacing colder water species like cod and whiting.

Uncertainties

We know that carbon dioxide and other greenhouse gases have increased as a result of human activity and it is now widely accepted that this has warmed the Earth's surface. We know that even with concerted action, greenhouse gas levels will continue to grow – leading to further warming. What is less certain though is the exact magnitude and timing of these changes and the regional and local details.

Much of the research is aimed at reducing these uncertainties, but our planet is a very complex system. There may be factors we haven't taken into consideration, we may have oversimplified some parts of

the system or, we may have underestimated the importance of one part of the system.

Such uncertainties mean that future effects could be less OR more severe than we currently estimate.

The key uncertainties

- Future emissions – economic and societal changes 100 years ahead are extremely difficult to predict.
- The carbon cycle – the oceans and plants absorb about half the carbon dioxide humans release into the atmosphere. Changes in climate will affect this absorption, and hence the amount of carbon dioxide remaining in the atmosphere. While these feedbacks are uncertain, our current understanding suggests that the ocean and land will take up less carbon.

There are further concerns that the absorbed carbon dioxide is making the oceans more acidic. This will damage marine organisms and could affect the oceans' ability to take up carbon dioxide.
- Tiny particles in the atmosphere from, for example, volcanoes, wildfires, dust and sea-salt spray can have positive and negative effects. Industry, transport and agriculture contribute to these particles in the atmosphere. While there are still considerable uncertainties, warming from greenhouse gases is expected to dominate over any cooling effects due to the presence of these particles in the atmosphere.
- Clouds can reflect incoming solar

radiation back into space, keeping heat out. But they can also prevent radiation escaping from the Earths surface, keeping heat in. So the effects can be positive or negative depending on the height, temperature and properties of the clouds, all of which vary in time and from place to place. Techniques for modelling and observing clouds, from the surface and space, have greatly improved in recent years, but they remain one of the biggest uncertainties in climate change.

- Water vapour. A warmer atmosphere can hold more moisture, which itself acts as a greenhouse gas and generates further warming (a positive feedback). Without this effect the projected warming would be only half the size. Uncertainties exist in the representation of water vapour in climate models, although considerable improvements have been made in recent years.

- Ice and snow. The melting of sea-ice and reduced snow cover in polar regions mean that the planet's surface absorbs more sunlight – this in turn induces more warming. Climate models represent sea-ice and snow quite crudely, though some can reproduce the observed decline in Arctic sea-ice.

- The oceans absorb large amounts of heat and carbon dioxide from the atmosphere. Ocean currents redistribute heat around the world and affect regional climate. Many features of ocean models have improved, but some are still poorly represented such as large-scale narrow currents along coastlines and flow through narrow channels.

- Regional predictions are much less certain than our estimates for global and large-scale change. This is because even our most advanced global climate models cannot model small features accurately.

Rapid climate change

Complex systems like the Earth can change abruptly and massively in unexpected ways. Small changes in one part of the system, such as the

amount of a greenhouse gas in the atmosphere, could trigger a dramatic response in another part, leading to rapid climate change.

An example of this is the North Atlantic overturning circulation, and which is driven by changes in heat and saltiness. This giant circulation moves warm, salty surface water from the tropics northwards and returns cold water to the south at depth. This gives western Europe its temperate climate. The heat it transfers to the atmosphere is equivalent to the power from about one million power stations.

In the past, disruptions to the North Atlantic overturning circulation coincided with rapid changes in air temperature (several degrees in a decade or so). Models predict that more fresh water, flowing into critical locations in the North Atlantic, could trigger a slowdown of the overturning circulation.

Such an event is thought to be unlikely to occur during this century, but if it should its impact on the climate of western Europe would be large. Therefore, research is being carried out on the probability of such changes (http://rapid.nerc.ac.uk).

Can we alter the course of climate change?

The greenhouse gases already emitted since the industrial revolution have committed us to a temperature rise of a degree or so. Carbon dioxide persists in the atmosphere for about 100 years, so concentrations respond very slowly to changes in emissions. Even if we significantly reduce carbon dioxide emissions, global temperature will take several decades to stabilise, and sea level several centuries or longer.

We do not really know how much climate change human society can cope with, so it is often argued that the precautionary principle should be invoked to reduce emissions by 60% over the next few decades. This should ensure that carbon dioxide levels do not exceed twice the pre-industrial level of 280ppm.

The Kyoto Protocol

At the climate summit meeting in Kyoto, Japan, in 1997, developed countries agreed to legally-binding national targets for reductions in greenhouse gas emissions. To reach the UK's commitment, carbon dioxide emissions must be 12.5% lower than in 1990, by 2012. The UK is still some distance from achieving the reductions. After years of wavering, Russia ratified the treaty in 2004. The protocol can now come into force. The United States, the world's biggest carbon dioxide emitter – responsible for one quarter of all carbon emissions worldwide – signed the agreement but did not ratify it.

The UK's Natural Environment Research Council funds and carries out impartial scientific research in the sciences of the environment. NERC trains the next generation of independent environmental scientists. NERC invests 28% of its total expenditure on climate change research through collaborative centres, dedicated research centres and in universities across the UK.

- This briefing note has been collated from work reported by many national and international organisations. Contributors: Kathy Maskell and Julia Slingo, from the NCAS Centre for Global Atmospheric Modelling; Louisa Watts and Alan Thorpe from the NCAS directorate; Geoff Jenkins from the Hadley Centre for Climate Prediction and Research; Asher Minns from the Tyndall Centre for Climate Change Research; Meric Srokosz from the NERC Rapid Climate Change programme. For a printed copy, please email: requests@nerc.ac.uk.

- The above information is from the Natural Environment Research Council (NERC). For more information visit their web site: www.nerc.ac.uk

Feeling the heat

Information from the United Nations Framework Convention on Climate Change (UNFCCC)

The average temperature of the earth's surface has risen by 0.6 degrees C since the late 1800s. It is expected to increase by another 1.4 to 5.8 degrees C by the year 2100 – a rapid and profound change. Even if the minimum predicted increase takes place, it will be larger than any century-long trend in the last 10,000 years.

The principal reason for the mounting thermometer is a century and a half of industrialisation: the burning of ever-greater quantities of oil, gasoline, and coal, the cutting of forests, and certain farming methods.

These activities have increased the amount of 'greenhouse gases' in the atmosphere, especially carbon dioxide, methane and nitrous oxide. Such gases occur naturally and are critical for life on earth; they keep some of the sun's warmth from reflecting back into space, and without them the world would be a cold and barren place. But in augmented and increasing quantities, these gases are pushing the global temperature to artificially high levels and altering the climate. The 1990s appear to have been the warmest decade of the last Millennium, and 1998 the warmest year.

Climate change can be difficult – you could ask the dinosaurs, if they weren't extinct. The prevailing theory is that they didn't survive when a giant meteorite struck the earth 65 million years ago, spewing so much dust into the air that sunlight was greatly reduced, temperatures plummeted, many plants didn't grow, and the food chain collapsed.

What happened to the dinosaurs is a rare example of climate change more rapid than humans are now inflicting on themselves . . . but not the only one. Research on ice cores and lake sediments shows that the climate system has suffered other abrupt fluctuations in the distant past – the climate appears to have 'tipping points' that can send it into sharp lurches and rebounds. Although scientists are still analysing what happened during those earlier events, it's clear that an overstressed world with 6.3 billion people is a risky place to be carrying out uncontrolled experiments with the climate.

The current warming trend is expected to cause extinctions. Numerous plant and animal species, already weakened by pollution and loss of habitat, are not expected to survive the next 100 years. Human beings, while not threatened in this way, are likely to face mounting difficulties. Recent severe storms, floods and droughts, for example, appear to show that computer models predicting more frequent 'extreme weather events' are on target.

The sea level rose on average by 10 to 20 cm during the 20th century, and an additional increase of 9 to 88 cm is expected by the year 2100. (Higher temperatures cause ocean volume to expand, and melting glaciers and ice caps add more water.) If the higher end of that scale is reached, the sea could overflow the heavily populated coastlines of such countries as Bangladesh, cause the

disappearance of some nations entirely (such as the island state of the Maldives), foul freshwater supplies for billions of people, and spur mass migrations.

Agricultural yields are expected to drop in most tropical and sub-tropical regions – and in temperate regions, too, if the temperature increase is more than a few degrees C. Drying of continental interiors, such as central Asia, the African Sahel, and the Great Plains of the United States, is also forecast. These changes could cause, at a minimum, disruptions in land use and food supply. And the range of diseases such as malaria may expand.

Global warming is a 'modern' problem – complicated, involving the entire world, tangled up with difficult issues such as poverty, economic development, and population growth. Dealing with it will not be easy. Ignoring it will be worse.

Over a decade ago, most countries joined an international treaty – the United Nations Framework Convention on Climate Change – to begin to consider what can be done to reduce global warming and to cope with whatever temperature increases are inevitable. In 1997 governments agreed to an addition to the treaty, called the Kyoto Protocol, which has more powerful (and legally binding) measures. The Protocol is expected to take effect soon. And, since 1988, an Inter-governmental Panel on Climate Change has reviewed scientific research and provided governments with summaries and advice on climate problems.

■ The above information is from the United Nations Framework Convention on Climate Change's website which can be found at www.unfccc.int
© *United Nations Framework Convention on Climate Change (UNFCCC)*

Global warming clock ticks faster

By Charles Clover, Environment Editor

Levels of carbon dioxide in the atmosphere are rising faster than at any time since records began, figures reveal.

Scientists cannot explain the unprecedented increase in 2002 and 2003 but they believe it is more likely to be the result of a natural phenomenon rather than a surge in burning of fossil fuels.

The rise suggests that global warming is speeding up.

A possibility raised by scientists at the Meteorological Office's Hadley Centre is that, as the world warms, it begins to release more carbon from natural sources which normally soak it up, such as forests, soils or oceans.

Dr Charles Keeling, 76, who began the longest-running carbon dioxide measurements at the Mauna Loa Observatory in Hawaii in 1958, said the unprecedented rise was 'a cause for concern'.

Carbon dioxide, mostly from the burning of coal, oil and gas, traps heat that otherwise would radiate into space. Temperatures increased by 0.6°C over the 20th century and an international panel of scientists has concluded that most of the warming was probably due to man-made greenhouse gases.

While it has yet to be proved categorically that such gases will cause the world to heat up over the next century, the debate among serious scientists is no longer whether the emissions are altering the climate, but by how much and whether the costs of repairing the damage are worth it.

Before the industrial era, the concentration of carbon dioxide in the atmosphere stood at around 280 parts per million (ppm), scientists have determined.

The average concentrations last year, according to the figures recorded by Dr Keeling's equipment 11,141ft up Mauna Loa, Hawaii's second highest volcano, were 375.64ppm.

The Mauna Loa records show that concentrations of the gas rose by 2.08ppm in 2002 and 2.54ppm in 2003, the first time successive years have seen an increase of more than 2 ppm.

According to the US agency which runs the observatory, the monthly average rises in carbon dioxide this year were higher than the 20-year average until June, when the rate of increase tailed off. The rise for this year is expected to be just under 2 ppm.

> **'The rise in the annual rate to above two parts per million for two consecutive years is a real phenomenon'**

Dr Keeling said: 'The rise in the annual rate to above two parts per million for two consecutive years is a real phenomenon.

'It is possible that this is the beginning of a natural process unprecedented in the record. This could be a weakening of the earth's carbon sinks, associated with the world warming, as part of a climate change feedback mechanism. It is a cause for concern.'

'Sinks' include things such as forests, soils and plankton. If they start releasing carbon, instead of

storing it, this is what climate scientists call a 'positive feedback'.

Peter Cox, the head of the carbon cycle group at the Met Office's Hadley Centre, said the figures for 2002 and 2003 looked like 'an interesting anomaly' which 'could not simply be explained by greater fossil fuel emissions'.

He added: 'There must be something else happening, adding carbon dioxide into the atmosphere. My guess is that there were extra forest fires in the northern hemisphere, and particularly a very hot summer in Europe.

'This led to a dieback in vegetation and an increase in release of carbon from the soil rather than more growing plants taking carbon out of the atmosphere which is usually the case in summer.'

Sir David King, Tony Blair's chief scientific adviser, will draw attention to the unprecedented rise in a speech on climate change at a Greenpeace event.

Tom Burke, visiting professor at Imperial College, London, and a former special adviser to the Conservative environment secretaries John Gummer and Michael Howard, said: 'The politically significant horizon is carbon dioxide at 400 parts per million – just because it's a big round number.

'If there is a rate change and we are looking at an increase of 2.5ppm a year, we'll cross that in 2015 instead of 2030. It brings the political threshold nearer for business and government.'

He said: 'If there is a change in the rate, the likelihood is that we have less time to take action. We are not taking the right action at the moment. We are not cutting emissions and investing in low carbon technologies.

'We're watching the clock and the clock is beginning to tick faster, as it seems to before a bomb goes off.'

© Telegraph Group Limited, London 2004

How does climate change affect me?

Information from the Worldwatch Institute

What are some of the impacts we can expect from climate change?
The impacts of climate change will vary from place to place, but we can expect more severe and frequent storms (such as hurricanes and ice storms), heat waves, floods, droughts and wildfires. Warmer temperatures will increase the range of disease-bearing mosquitoes, while also increasing the range and numbers of insects and other agricultural pests, such as weeds. Melting glaciers and expanding sea water (water expands as it warms) will further raise sea level, inundating low-lying islands and flooding coastal areas, while warmer ocean temperatures will kill many if not most of the world's coral reefs. Such events, in turn, will influence our food supply, our access to clean water, our health, and the economic and social conditions of families and communities around the world.

As ecosystems become further stressed by climate change, species extinction will accelerate. Many of the species lost will be seemingly 'insignificant' plants and insects, but we will also lose plants that could cure diseases, and large animals such as polar bears, which rely on winter ice as a platform to hunt for food. Warmer winters could mean reduced snow pack for some regions, reducing water supplies and the output of hydropower dams in the north-western US, for example, and shortening if not eliminating ski seasons in some regions such as New England. The regional or national economic impacts of such changes could be significant.

Many such changes are already being seen around the world. For example, the number of weather-

related disasters experienced world-wide every year has been increasing over the past few decades. In the United States, the number of such disasters experienced each decade has risen fivefold since the 1970s. During the course of this century, average global surface temperatures are projected to increase at a rate unprecedented over at least the past 10,000 years, and scientists believe that rising temperatures could further increase the intensity and frequency of extreme weather events.

Could climate change ever 'wipe us out'?

Past changes in climate have caused glaciers to advance and rivers to freeze. Even regional temperature fluctuations have contributed to the deaths of millions of people and the demise of civilisations, as in the cases of the Irish Potato Famine and the Vikings' departure from Greenland. But humans can move and adapt far more easily than most other species, and are unlikely to be wiped out – even by abrupt changes.

At the same time, it's important to realise that even relatively small changes in average global tem-

perature can have significant impacts on weather patterns, agricultural productivity, water resources, and the spread of disease – and thus on millions of individual people. Climate change will have a lot of negative impacts, like the extinction of many plant and animal species, the spread of disease-carrying insects, more frequent and intense heat waves, floods, droughts, and wildfires. Already, the World Health Organization blames climate change for an estimated 150,000 human deaths every year.

Should I be worried about climate change? Will it affect me personally?

Rising global temperature means more than just extra time to wear shorts and sandals. An increase of just a few degrees in average temperature can cause dramatic changes in conditions that are important to the quality of life – and even the Earth's ability to support life. We may not always see or feel it directly, but climate change affects us all. For one person it might mean paying more for food because flooding or drought has damaged crops. For another it might mean a higher risk of contracting a disease like malaria, which spreads more easily in warm, wet climates. Someone else might face losing her home or even life in a catastrophic weather disaster made worse by global warming.

Almost everyone is vulnerable to the effects of weather-related disasters, but people in poor countries face a far greater threat due to risk factors that include inadequate housing located on flood plains and steep hillsides, weak healthcare systems, and heavy economic dependence on agriculture. It is not uncommon for single weather events, such as tropical cyclones and floods, to kill thousands of people in regions such as South Asia, southern China, and Central America. If the warming continues for years and sea levels rise as predicted, then a great many people will become climate refugees – because their homes and countries will be under water. Rising sea levels will also affect people in US coastal regions, from the Outer Banks of North Carolina and much of Florida, to Louisiana, to California. Already, rising seas are forcing communities in Alaska to move inland, at very high cost to the state.

What can I do?

What can we do right now to slow climate change and make a real difference?

While it's impossible for any one individual to prevent global warming, we each have a direct impact on the conditions that allow warming to occur. We can pledge to do our part to conserve energy and pollute less. Whether at home, on our commute to work or school, in the office, or at the store, there are things we can do to lessen our contribution to climate change.

Examples of things you can do include turning off lights and computers when they are not in use, using public transportation or carpooling, driving less, recycling, purchasing energy efficient appliances or a more fuel-efficient car, buying food grown locally, insulating your water heater and home, and choosing 'green' electricity from a company selling power generated from renewable sources such as the wind or sun, which is now possible in many areas.

For additional practical ways to lessen your impact on global warming see Worldwatch's guide to consumer items, Good Stuff, at www.worldwatch.org/pubs/goodstuff/ Also, see the Green Ribbon Pledge at www.greenribbonpledge.org/pledge/index.html, and the Center for a New American Dream's Turn the Tide Campaign at www.newdream.org/turnthetide/ These two sites will allow you to calculate your energy savings and track the positive impact you are having on the planet as you make better choices.

Another important way to act on climate change is by voting and supporting candidates who are serious about reducing greenhouse gas emissions. Also, encourage your current state and national legislators to support legislation that will slow climate change.

■ The above information is from Worldwatch Institute's website: www.worldwatch.org

© Worldwatch Institute

How much climate change can we bear?

Information from Greenpeace

The stated goal of the United Nations Framework Convention on Climate Change (1992) is to avoid 'dangerous climate change'. We are committed to 1.2-1.3°C of global average temperature rise above pre-industrial levels from the greenhouse gases (ghgs) that we have pumped into the atmosphere. Keeping global average temperature rise below 2°C should be the goal of climate change policy.[1] While this is certainly dangerous to the millions of people who will be affected, it is probably the best we can do.

Two degrees Centigrade global average warming:

■ Threatens many tens of millions of people with increased risk of hunger, hundreds of millions with increased malaria risk, millions with increased flooding and billions with increased risk of water shortage.[2,3]
– Damages fall largely on the poorest and developing countries, particularly in sub-Saharan Africa, South Asia, and parts of SE Asia and Latin America.

■ Risks melting of major ice sheets with commitments to many metres of sea-level rise over several centuries, particularly the Greenland ice sheet (7 metres), and the West Antarctic Ice Sheet (WAIS) (5-7 metres). Greenland melting is accelerating and rapid melting acceleration of the glaciers from a large sector of the WAIS is now observed to be occurring and may presage the dynamic collapse of this component of the ice sheet.
– Ensuing sea-level rise threatens large populations everywhere and particularly low-lying areas in developing countries such as Bangladesh, South China, and low-lying island states everywhere, not to mention 'the low countries' (Belgium, the Nether-

lands, NW Germany), and south-east UK.

- Threatens damage to major ecosystems from the Arctic and Antarctic to the tropics.
  – Loss of forests and species will affect the lives of all with economic costs falling disproportionately on the poor and developing countries

Keep warming below 2°C – What CAN be avoided?

- Limit damages to coral reefs
- Limit risk of major ecological damages globally
- Limit both rate and extent of sea-level rise over many centuries
- Limit risk of Greenland ice sheet collapse
- Limit West Antarctic Ice Sheet instability risk
- Hunger, water scarcity and disease risk seem to accelerate with higher temperature, taking into account future economic growth and increased wealth

How to get there?

- It is still technologically, economically and scientifically possible to limit global temperature rise to less than 2°C above pre-industrial levels, but time is not on our side. We are within a decade or two of closing off those options with known technological means.
- Estimates of the 'sensitivity' of the climate to increases in ghgs are expressed in terms of the temperature response of the climate system to a doubling of pre-industrial levels of greenhouse gases in the atmosphere, expressed in carbon-dioxide equivalence in parts-per-million (ppm). Pre-industrial levels of carbon dioxide were about 270 million ppm. Today we are at about 379 ppm. The mid-line estimate of the response to the climate of a doubling of ghg concentrations to 550 ppm has been 2.5°C increase. So, we have said that our best guess is that the climate sensitivity is 2.5°C.
- However, recent studies have revealed that the new best guess is that the climate sensitivity is

in fact closer to 3.2°C, which means that the response from the climate to the anticipated rise in ghgs will be even more dramatic than previously thought. We have to act even faster and take more dramatic action if we are to avoid the damage associated with a 2°C global average temperature rise. This means that for now we have to aim for stabilising ghgs in the atmosphere at a level below 400 ppm and then seek to bring them down as rapidly as possible if we are to have a reasonable chance of keeping global temperature rise below 2°C.

- To meet these goals dramatic reductions in greenhouse gas emissions are needed, and they are needed soon. From a moral, legal and practical perspective, the initial burden of emissions reductions has to fall on industrialised countries. Reductions of at least 30% on 1990 levels (the 'baseline' year for the Kyoto Protocol) by 2020 from industrialised countries are required, with a target of at least 75% reductions by mid-century.
- Globally, we need to bring total emissions back to 1990 levels by about 2020 and then reduce them by 50% by mid-century. This means that rapidly industrialising economies like China, India, Mexico, Brazil, South Africa, Indonesia, Malaysia and others need to start reducing their emissions soon.
- The consequences of delay in the process of reducing emissions means that we will face a dire

global emergency in the 2020s which will require rates of emissions reductions which in the past have only been associated with massive economic collapse, i.e., with the collapse of the Soviet Union. We must not be forced to choose between economic catastrophe and climate catastrophe . . . the most likely outcome in that case would be both, and we have a good chance of avoiding this if we act now.

- The USA must be brought into the system sooner rather than later. If the US carries on with business-as-usual, the rest of the industrialised world 'runs out' of emissions some time around 2025.

Reference

1 http://www.climatenetwork.org/docs/CAN-adequacy30102002.pdf
2 Hare, B (2003) Assessment of Knowledge on Impacts of Climate Change – Contribution to the Specification of Art. 2 of the UNFCCC: Impacts on Ecosystems, Food Production, Water and Socio-economic System. www.wbgu.de/wbgu_sn2003_ex01.pdf
3 See M Parry, N Arnell, T McMichael, R Nicholls, P Martens, S Kovats, M Livermore, C Rosenzweig, A Iglesias and G Fischer, Millions at Risk: Defining Critical Climate Change Threats and Targets, *Global Environmental Change* 11.3 (2001): 1-3.

- The above information is from Greenpeace's website which can be found at www.greenpeace.org.uk

Emissions of carbon dioxide: EU comparison

Tonnes per capita	1990	2000	% change 1990-2000
Belgium	11.8	12.4	4.7%
Luxembourg		12.3	-
Finland	12.5	12.0	-3.9%
Irish Republic	9.0	11.6	28.4%
Netherlands	10.7	10.9	2.1%
Germany	12.8	10.4	-18.2%
Greece	8.4	10.2	20.7%
Denmark	10.2	9.9	-3.3%
United Kingdom	10.3	9.1	-11.2%
Austria	8.1	8.2	1.1%
Italy	7.7	8.0	3.7%
Spain	5.9	7.8	32.8%
France	6.9	6.8	-1.7%
Portugal	4.5	6.3	41.6%
Sweden	6.6	6.3	-3.9%

Source: EEA, Social Trends, Crown copyright

The impact of climate change

Information from People & Planet

Climate change is happening now and will affect all of us. Even if we cut our emissions of carbon dioxide (CO_2) by 60-90% today, as recommended by international scientists, we still won't escape the effects of the massive increase in CO_2 in the atmosphere that we have already created. We can't say exactly what the impact of these emissions will be, especially at the local level, but we can make predictions and construct reliable models that give us likely scenarios.

1. Water: rising tides and increased scarcity

The temperature of the world's oceans is rising. This rising heat will cause the sea water to expand, raising tide levels, causing coastal flooding especially in low-lying river delta and island areas. It is predicted that this combined with the extra water released from melting glaciers and ice caps will cause a 15-95cm rise in sea levels by 2100 on top of the 10-25cm already experienced.

- This is enough to submerge many low-lying island nations entirely – one of the Carteret atolls of Papua New Guinea has already been cut in half by the ocean.
- Tuvalu in the South Pacific has concluded a deal with New Zealand to evacuate the entire 10,000 population. For now, only 75 people per year will leave the islands.
- Between now and 2020, up to three-quarters of the world's population, most of them living in poor countries, could be at risk from drought or flood.
- A 50cm rise will bankrupt Venezuela.
- A 1 metre rise will displace 80% of Guyana's population.
- Many developing countries have their main cities in coastal areas, so these will be the first to go, causing a devastating destruction of infrastructure in those countries least able to deal with it.

Bangladesh:

In September 1998 two-thirds of this Asian country was submerged by major floods. Twenty-one million people were left homeless. On current predictions, a fifth of Bangladesh will be drowned entirely and the rest regularly experience floods on the scale of 1998 by 2100.

Flooding will be exacerbated by exaggeration of the world's rainfall patterns. This means that wet areas will become wetter, but it also means dry areas will become drier. Water scarcity for drinking and industry is already a problem for 1.7 billion people. By 2050, it is likely to be a problem for up to 3.6 billion, with Lake Chad already 95% disappeared, and other sources likely to dry up. This raises the possibility of water wars, and desperation for billions of people.

2. Agriculture: hunger and loss

The lack of rain in drier areas will soon negate any of the positive effects of more CO_2 (increased plant growth), and it is probable that we will see the same kind of massive crop failures experienced in northern Africa recently spreading around the world. Drought could become a permanent state for countries like Somalia. This means hunger, famine and severe food shortages.

Flooding, expected to wipe out the one third of the world's crop lands that are in coastal or low-lying areas, will also have a major impact. Floods in Mozambique in 1998 during El Niño wiped out all 'plant genetic resources' according to the UN Food and Agriculture Organisation, causing terrible stress on food resources. The Hadley centre predicts 30 million more people will be hungry because of climate change by 2050, with 300 million in sub-Saharan Africa suffering from chronic malnutrition by 2010.

3. Disrupting ecosystems: climate change to kill up to 1 million species

Scientists at Leeds University predict that over the next fifty years, climate change could drive a quarter of land animals and plants into extinction. More than 1 million species could be lost by 2050. Much of that loss – more than one in ten of all plants and animals – is irreversible, because of the greenhouse gases already in the atmosphere.

As the earth heats up, climate zones will shift outwards from the

equator. This means that countries to the north of the equator like the UK will find themselves living in the recognisable climate of countries far closer to the equator, as will southern countries like New Zealand. Within our lifetimes, London may have the climate of southern France, while the scorching deserts of northern Africa may creep into Europe. Per degree centigrade rise in world temperatures, zones will move approximately 300 km outwards.

In 1998, sunfish and seahorses were seen for the first time in the warming waters off the British coast, and unconfirmed sightings of two great white sharks off Cornwall this year have led to concerns that this disruption to the ecosystem is happening faster than expected. Vast swathes of the earth may become empty of life. The golden toad of Costa Rica is already described as climate change's first known victim. This species has become extinct due to the loss of habitat caused by climate change. Birds, which have the greatest chance of escape, could in theory move to a more suitable climate, but the trees and other habitat they need for survival are unlikely to keep pace.

4. Changing weather patterns: creating unnatural disasters

More energy from the sun trapped in the weather system by CO_2 emissions means the exaggeration of its force and unpredictability. The kind of disasters already seen are likely to take increasingly extreme forms, with storm surges and prolonged droughts added onto hurricanes and cyclones, as the extra energy whips up the system.

Hurricane Mitch:

In October/November 1998, 10,000 people died in Honduras and Nicaragua as hurricane Mitch hit people with 155 miles per hour winds. Three million people were displaced, and the cost of the damage totalled 70% of Honduras' income.

This will cause massive damage to infrastructure and lives. The UN predicts that 25 million environmental refugees were created in the 1990s, with no official status, forced from their homes by 'natural' disasters

More energy from the sun trapped in the weather system by CO_2 emissions means the exaggeration of its force and unpredictability

exacerbated or caused by climate change. The New Economics Foundation suggests that the cost of paying for human-caused 'natural' disasters could overtake the income of the world economy by 2065. According to Munich Reinsurance, during the 1960s there were 16 climate-related natural disasters. During the 1990s there were 70.

El Niño:

The El Niño phenomenon, which causes extreme weather conditions, used to occur every seven years on average. In 1982-3 it brought the most serious conditions ever seen, causing $8 billion damage and 1,000 dead. But from 1991 to 1995 some kind of El Niño occurred every year, and re-appeared in 1998 with torrential rains, droughts and flash floods.

5. Human health: disease

In hotter, wetter temperatures, diseases thrive. Malaria and other insect-borne diseases are expected to massively increase their spread and range as more humid weather allows previously untouched countries to experience so-called 'tropical' diseases, and those already suffering are hit harder. It has been suggested that 60% of the world will be in a malaria zone by 2100. Rift valley fever has already been seen to jump species to infect humans in times of great heat and water pressure, and this is a danger for other infections too. As flooding and habitat damage encourage shifting populations, disease will be even further spread, and overcrowded city slums extend further. Malnutrition from food scarcity, and the lack of water, is also likely to have a major impact on human health.

6. A vicious cycle

More frightening even than these likely impacts, is the possibility of

what is called 'positive feedback'. This is when the increase in greenhouse gases causes other, less predictable reactions than simple heating, reinforcing and accelerating the impact of the changes outlined above. It is even possible that extreme and unanticipated changes may occur, causing dramatic and catastrophic shifts. Some possible examples of this are:

The Big Melt:

The world's ice caps are already melting. There has been a 40% drop in the amount of Arctic ice since the 1970s. Were this effect to spread, and the northern ice fields melt, a rise in sea levels of up to seven metres would occur. This would not simply overwhelm low-lying countries like Bangladesh, but also major western cities such as London, Rome and New York.

Permafrost:

Permafrost covers around 450 billion tonnes of carbon stored in dead vegetation. Were this to melt, that massive carbon store would be uncovered, and the level of CO_2 in the atmosphere would increase dramatically.

Water evaporation:

As the seas heat up, more surface water will evaporate. Since water vapour is in itself a natural greenhouse gas, this will thicken the 'greenhouse' further, and re-inforce the damage done by CO_2.

Losing the forests:

Not only does the destruction of forest areas mean less capacity to convert CO_2, but the act of burning the plant life to make way for agricultural land releases massive amounts of CO_2 into the atmosphere, as trees are natural sources of carbon. Modelling by the Hadley centre suggests that due to changing climate, forests such as the Amazon may experience dieback, and thus become net contributors of carbon to the atmosphere as the forest burns or decays. This again has a multiplication effect.

■ The above information is from People & Planet's website: www.peopleandplanet.org

© People & Planet

We are all losers in the greenhouse world

By George Marshall

The literature of climate change regularly asks who will be the 'winners and losers' in the greenhouse world. Any websearch finds over a thousand documents using the phrase, including papers by United Nations agencies, leading scientists, and the UK Hadley Centre. Politicians, including Tony Blair, often speak in this way of climate change as though it is a sporting event, peppering their speeches with references to 'opportunities' and 'challenges'.

In terms of social justice such language is very revealing. The gain of one group as a result of the removal of benefit from another group is the most basic definition of crime. When we talk of winners and losers from climatic collapse we are using the language of criminality.

The impact on world food production is a case in point. Research published last year predicted that climate change would cut food production in developing countries by up to a quarter by 2050. The 40 countries worst hit by falling yields are all in the South and have a combined population of over a billion people.

At the same time, according to the Intergovernmental Panel on Climate Change, warmer weather could bring huge increases in food production to northern latitudes. The potential increase in yields in Canada alone is as great as the decline in India. The redistribution of productivity will be the equivalent of shipping 130 million tonnes of grain each year from one of the world's poorest countries to one of the world's richest.

There are many other ways that climate change further widens the existing cruelties and inequities in the world. The direct impacts of increasingly extreme weather events are being borne by the poorest and most vulnerable people. 98% of the deaths from so-called 'natural

disasters' are in the South. In 1998 alone they created 25 million refugees. Christian Aid, one of the few aid organisations that appreciates the full implications of climate change for its work, argues that we should now regard all severe weather events as 'unnatural disasters'.

It is hard for us to appreciate the scale of the problem given the extremely patchy coverage in the Western media. There was constant coverage of the floods this year in central Europe: we heard next to nothing of the floods last year in Algeria, which killed over a thousand people. Deaths in India, Africa, and China have next to no news value at all.

It is a mistake, though, to regard individual weather events as the main impact of climate change. The shifting of coastlines, rainfall

patterns, and seasons will have far greater ramifications in the longer term. Over the next 50 years these will force the displacement of 60 million people in India and China. Even if greenhouse gas emissions are successfully cut, sea levels will continue to rise by up to half a metre, displacing 15 million people in Bangladesh alone.

Such vast movements in human populations bring the further threat of war. In a report published last year, the UK Ministry of Defence recognised for the first time climate change as a major cause of future conflicts. It raised particular concerns over the possibility of water wars. By 2015, 3 billion people will be living in areas without enough water. In the Middle East water is already one of the main sources of conflict. Turkey's strategy of diverting water from the Tigris and Euphrates rivers with dams and irrigation systems is regarded by the downstream countries of Iraq and Syria as an act of outright aggression.

Rich countries cynically believe, in the midst of such conflict and suffering, that they will be the 'winners' because they believe that they can exploit any instability to extend their own economic and political interests. According to the neo-liberal world view, the 'losers' will be those countries with the weak and vulnerable economies that cannot adapt. The 'winners' will be those with the strongest economies which can ride out the uncertainties and costs of climate chaos. By the perverted logic of a junkie, the best line of defence against climate change is a strong economy, and the best way to support a strong economy is by maintaining the supply of cheap oil.

With world oil production due to peak in 2005, controlling this increasingly scarce resource has become a preoccupation of foreign policy and multilateral development funding. It is for this reason that the UK government is currently preparing to hand over millions of pounds of subsidies to fund British Petroleum to build pipelines that will transport oil and gas from its Caspian reserves to European markets. John Browne, the managing director of BP, admitted that the project cannot go ahead without government grants, export credit guarantees, and multilateral credit, which, in an unguarded moment, he called 'free money'.

The 1,750 km pipelines through Azerbaijan, Georgia and Turkey would transport a million barrels of oil a day and 730 million cubic metres of gas a day, enough to fuel every power station in the UK. The oil and gas, once burnt, would produce two and a half times more carbon dioxide than the reductions required of the UK under the Kyoto Protocol.

The politics of oil production require that the British government supports this project even if it contradicts and undermines climate change policy. The UK and US intend to establish a decisive control over Caspian oil production, and need to ensure that the resource supplies European rather than Chinese or Russian markets. Razi Nurullayev from the Azerbaijan Society for Democratic Reform confirms that the project is 'much more political than economic'. It is, he says, a reflection of Azerbaijan's determination to align itself with the US and Europe after 70 years of Russian domination.

However, the pipeline countries may well be replacing one form of colonialism for another. The agreement signed between BP and the Turkish government exempts BP from obligations under any current or future Turkish law that may threaten the project's profits, including environmental, social and human rights legislation. The company is allowed to establish a militarised corridor along the pipeline, which would effectively be outside the national government's jurisdiction for the lifetime of the project.

Nick Hildyard from the Corner House, one of six organisations in a coalition monitoring the pipeline, observes wryly: 'Turkey is now divided into three countries: the area where Turkish law applies; the Kurdish areas under military rule; and a strip running the entire length of the country from North to South, where BP is the effective government.'

In October, activists from Alaska, Colombia and Scotland met with groups from the pipeline region in London and warned them to expect harassment, bribery, assassinations, and environmental destruction under BP's rule.

The issues they raised – expropriation of wealth, destruction of livelihoods, forced relocation, and political instability – directly parallel the wider social justice issues of climate change. Although patterns of domination and exploitation are a common motif in global economic relations, the similarities are not a coincidence. An economic system dependent on a single energy source is clearly in the interest of a global elite that believes it can control its supply. The lack of equity is not a by-product of this system, it is a planned and deliberate part of it.
■ George Marshall works with Rising Tide, a national network of grassroots groups campaigning against climate change. www.risingtide.org.uk This article first appeared in Friends of the Earth's supporter magazine, *Earthmatters*.

© *Friends of the Earth*

Abrupt climate change

Information from Friends of the Earth

Yes, I know climate change is happening, but it'll just be gradual warming by a couple of degrees – warmer days in Britain – sounds good to me.'

Agree? Well you are not alone, but you are wrong.

This article explains why climate change is a serious issue and focuses on the possible effects of a rapid change in global climate.

Why now?
Whilst the possibility of climate change has been considered for some time, recent stories in the media have highlighted the disastrous consequences of an abrupt change in global climate. A BBC *Horizon* programme suggested Britain may

Friends of the Earth

face a new Ice Age,[1] a report from the Pentagon examined the potential violent conflict and mass movement of refugees resulting from abrupt climate change,[2] and the Hollywood film *The Day After Tomorrow*, shows apocalyptic scenes supposedly resulting from abrupt climate change.[3]

Global temperatures rose by an average of about 0.6°C over the last century[4] and in 2003 there were unusual climate-related events worldwide: droughts in Southern Africa, heatwaves in India, huge forest fires in Siberia and flooding in parts of South America.[5]

Global average temperatures are currently predicted to increase by between 1.4 and 5.8°C by 2100.[6] The idea that climate change is harmless and will just mean 'nicer weather' is wrong and dangerous. A warming of just 2 to 3°C in the next 100 years would put 3 billion people at risk from water shortage, an extra 300 million facing the threat of malaria and 100 million more in danger because of coastal flooding.[7] Even more lives could be at risk if the climate changes over a shorter time scale – so called abrupt climate change.

What do we mean by abrupt climate change?

Imagine a car being pushed slowly up a hill; it may reach the top of the hill and then suddenly fall down the other side, at a rate much faster than it was being pushed. In scientific terms abrupt climate change occurs when a climate system crosses a threshold and enters a new state at a rate faster than can be explained by cause. The climate may change dramatically over just 10 to 20 years[8] – so fast that human and natural systems have difficulty adjusting.[9] And once the threshold has been reached it may be hard or even impossible to return to the previous state.

One possible example of abrupt climate change would occur as a result of the weakening or halting of the thermohaline circulation. The thermohaline circulation is the natural movement of water in the Atlantic Ocean, driven by temperature and salinity, that brings warm water northward and produces a more temperate climate in Northern Europe, including the UK. (This is subtly different from the Gulf Stream – the wind driven movement of water in the Atlantic Ocean which also moves warm water north – which will not be affected by changes in the amount of fresh water entering the N. Atlantic.) If, as predicted, climate change was to raise global temperatures it is likely there would be an increase in the amount of freshwater flowing into the North Atlantic from the rivers of Russia and the melting of glaciers in Greenland. This freshwater would lie on top of the denser salt water and reduce the heat transfer by acting as a cap. It would also reduce the salinity of the water and potentially at a certain threshold, eventually stop the North Atlantic water from sinking, halting the circulation entirely. The result for the climate of North-west Europe would be dramatic, with temperatures no longer rising as expected with global 'warming', but suddenly cooling.

Such a change could cool down selective areas of the globe by 3°C to 5°C.[10]

Unfortunately, there is currently insufficient data to say how likely this scenario is. Most climate models predict that there will be a weakening in the present warming influence of the thermohaline circulation, but there is a considerable spread in their predictions and two models show no change at all.[11] However, this does not indicate that change is unlikely – it just means we don't yet know enough about the climate system to predict what will happen. Recent observations at a few key locations suggest that significant changes are happening in the North Atlantic. A weakening of the thermohaline circulation may already be in process.[12]

To better understand abrupt climate change, and in particular the thermohaline circulation, the Natural Research Council has invested £20 million in a six-year scientific study of rapid climate change – RAPID. This work is due for completion in 2007, and will hopefully go a long way to clarifying the current uncertainty.

What other abrupt changes are possible?

There are other climate systems which may trigger abrupt climate change, which are poorly understood. One of these is the Agulhas current – a system which feeds water from the Indian Ocean into the South Atlantic in a series of eddies. Their influence on the thermohaline circulation is not well understood, but simple models have suggested that if this process stopped the thermohaline circulation could become more susceptible to disruption.[13] It is also possible that climate change may influence both the frequency and the amplitude of the El Niño. This periodic and temporary disruption of the ocean-atmosphere climate system in the tropical Pacific has important consequences for weather around the globe[14] – a prime example of the interconnectedness of oceanic currents and atmospheric conditions. Aside from all the other implications for the climate, change in the El Niño might disrupt the Agulhas current, which could in turn disturb the thermohaline circulation.

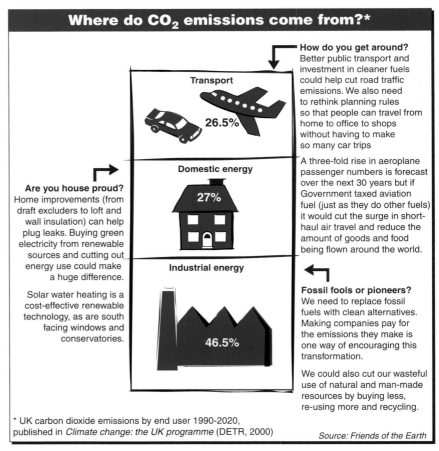

Where do CO₂ emissions come from?*

Transport — 26.5%

Domestic energy — 27%

Industrial energy — 46.5%

How do you get around? Better public transport and investment in cleaner fuels could help cut road traffic emissions. We also need to rethink planning rules so that people can travel from home to office to shops without having to make so many car trips

A three-fold rise in aeroplane passenger numbers is forecast over the next 30 years but if Government taxed aviation fuel (just as they do other fuels) it would cut the surge in short-haul air travel and reduce the amount of goods and food being flown around the world.

Are you house proud? Home improvements (from draft excluders to loft and wall insulation) can help plug leaks. Buying green electricity from renewable sources and cutting out energy use could make a huge difference.

Solar water heating is a cost-effective renewable technology, as are south facing windows and conservatories.

Fossil fools or pioneers? We need to replace fossil fuels with clean alternatives. Making companies pay for the emissions they make is one way of encouraging this transformation.

We could also cut our wasteful use of natural and man-made resources by buying less, re-using more and recycling.

* UK carbon dioxide emissions by end user 1990-2020, published in *Climate change: the UK programme* (DETR, 2000)

Source: Friends of the Earth

Another potential scenario for rapid climate change focuses on the vast quantities of methane that are deposited below the ocean and permafrost. Methane is approximately 20 times as powerful a greenhouse gas as carbon dioxide,[15] and this submarine store is enormous – more than a thousand times that currently in the atmosphere.[16] It is easy to see that if these deposits were disturbed (by changes in sea floor temperature and pressure), the resultant rapid, massive methane release would have huge implications for the climate. Some scientists have suggested that previous episodes of global climate change were linked to releases of the submarine methane.[17] Again, however, the likelihood of this scenario leading to rapid climate change is unknown, and the most recent IPCC report quotes a study which found little evidence of such an event within the previous 50,000 years.[18]

A much discussed topic is the melting of the West Antarctic ice sheet, which would raise global sea levels by 5 metres and lead to abrupt climate change. Scientists have recently discovered that the ice sheet is 'currently undergoing rapid and dramatic change in particular regions' and that it has a history of 'dramatic fluctuation' in size. It is unclear whether the observed recent changes are natural variability or suggest an impending collapse. This question, and the impact of melting on global climate, are also being extensively researched.[19]

Will there also be an increase in extreme weather events?

Climate change will not only cause changes in average temperatures, but will also trigger more so-called extreme weather events. Global warming is predicted to change the frequency, intensity, and duration of extreme events leading to more hot days, heat waves and heavy precipitation, and cyclones might become stronger.[20]

As an example of extreme weather events March 2004 saw the first ever recorded cyclone in the South Atlantic. Tropical Cyclone Catarina hit Brazil, causing considerable destruction and loss of life.

This event is broadly consistent with some predictions for the impact of global warming on this region and is being intensely analysed by the scientific community to try and establish whether it is a signal of climate change.[21]

What abrupt climate change has there been in the past?

The Younger Dryas event, which happened around 12,000 years ago, resulted in an abrupt drop of temperatures of between 2 and 10°C.[22] Icebergs extended to the south of Portugal.[23] To put this timeline in a human perspective, the end of the Stone Age roughly co-incided with the end of this Ice Age, and it was only as recently as around 5,500 years ago that the first human civilisations emerged.[24]

A similar abrupt drop in temperatures happened 8,200 years ago. It was not so severe, but scientists have suggested that 'if a similar cooling event occurred today, it would be catastrophic'.[25]

The medieval warm period was a rapid period of global warming 1,000 years ago. It was on a much smaller scale than the previous two events, but was still sufficient for the Norse people to settle on Greenland.[26]

A further 'little ice age' occurred about 700 years ago. The Norse abandoned Greenland and over the next few hundred years 'severe winters had profound agricultural, economic, and political impacts in Europe'.[27]

During the current 10,000-year interglacial warm period further abrupt regional climate changes have occurred. These included abrupt shifts in hurricane frequency, changes in flood regimes and drought.[28] There is some evidence that such events were linked to the collapse of civilisations including the Akkadian empire in Mesopotamia 4,200 years ago, and the Mayan empire in central America 1,500 years ago.[29]

Such historic changes in climate can be linked with previous changes in carbon dioxide levels.

In 2000 the level of carbon dioxide in the atmosphere was 368 ppm. The IPCC predicts that by 2100 this figure will have risen to between 540 ppm and 970 ppm.[30]

The current levels of CO_2 are far larger than have been seen in the last 420,000 years.[31] It is likely that the current levels are the highest they have ever been for the past 40 million to 50 million years.[32] The predicted increase this century to 540-970 ppm will take us even further outside previous boundaries. It is clear that if these predictions are fulfilled we will push the global climate into uncharted waters. The possibility of reaching an unexpected threshold and triggering abrupt climate change is very real.

You're just scaremongering...

If you think that this is just Friends of the Earth talking up the facts, you might be interested to see what some others have to say about climate change:

Tony Blair, Prime Minister, described climate change as: 'very, very critical indeed . . . [it is] the single most important long-term issue that we face as a global community'.[33]

David King, Chief Scientific Adviser to the government, said: 'In my view, climate change is the most severe problem that we are facing today, more serious even than the threat of terrorism.'[34]

Even the recent report for the Pentagon recommended that 'because of the potentially dire consequences, the risk of abrupt climate change, although uncertain and quite possibly small, should be elevated beyond a scientific debate to a U.S. national security concern'.[35]

If that's right, why isn't anyone doing anything?

The fundamental problem is that climate change, and particularly abrupt climate change, is simply a bigger and conceptually more difficult problem than society has ever had to face before. Incremental policy and behavioural changes are insufficient when you consider that by the time the results of climate change have been noticed it may already be too late to take action.

We must rise to the challenge, and indeed many individuals, organisations and governments are already trying to make a difference. However, for politicians to make the big changes needed, they need public support – and this is where you come in. We need to aim towards a so-called carbon neutral society. Some of the required changes are win-win situations. For instance moving away from fossil fuels to renewable sources of energy will increase our security of supply as well as tackling climate change. Other choices will be tougher, but nevertheless we need to face them. All energy production has a cost – the question is would you rather a coal-fired power station or wind turbines? So, use democracy to encourage and support your MP to take positive action on climate change. As an individual you can effect change for yourself, your family, friends and workplace.

To find out more about what you can do either give us a ring on 0808 800 1111 or check out the Friends of the Earth website: www.foe.co.uk/campaigns/climate/

References

1 *The Big Chill, Horizon.* BBC Two, Thursday 13 November 2003, 9pm.
2 *An Abrupt Climate Change Scenario and Its Implications for United States National Security.* Peter Schwartz and Doug Randall. October 2003.
3 *The Day After Tomorrow,* Twentieth Century Fox. Released May 28 2004.
4 *Climate Change 2001: Summary for Policy Makers.* Contribution of Working Group I to the Third Assessment Report of the Inter-governmental Panel on Climate Change. 2001.
5 National Environmental Satellite and Information Service, *Significant Climate Anomalies and Events in 2003.*
6 See Ref 4.
7 *Millions at Risk.* Martin Parry, Director of the Jackson Environment Institute at the University of

---

We must rise to the challenge, and indeed many individuals, organisations and governments are already trying to make a difference

---

East Anglia and co-chair of IPCC Working Group II et al.
8 *Abrupt Climate Change: Can Society Cope?* Professor Mike Hulme, Tyndall Centre for Climate Change Research, Working Paper 30. March 2003.
9 Rapid Climate Change: Scientific Challenges and the new NERC programme. M.A. Srokosz. *Phil. Trans. R. Soc. Lond.* A (2003) 361, 2061-2078. 22 July 2003.
10 Abrupt Climate Change: Should We Be Worried? Robert B. Gagosian, President and Director, Woods Hole Oceanographic Institution. Prepared for a panel on abrupt climate change at the World Economic Forum Davos, Switzerland. 27 January 2003.
11 See Ref 9.
12 Ibid.
13 Ibid.
14 NOAA El Niño Page, US Department of Commerce National Oceanic and Atmospheric Administration. Last updated 28 February. www.elnino.noaa.gov
15 *Climate Change 2001: The Scientific Basis.* Contribution of Working Group I to the Third Assessment Report of the Inter-governmental Panel on Climate Change. 2001.

See Table 6.7 Over 100 years the global warming potential of methane is 23 times that of carbon dioxide.
16 *Climate Change 2001: Synthesis Report.* Contribution of Working Group I, II and III to the Third Assessment Report of the Inter-governmental Panel on Climate Change. 2001. See Section 4.12.
17 For example, Richard J. Behl, California State University, Long Beach, California.
18 See Ref 15, Section 4.2.1.1.
19 The West Antarctic Ice Sheet Initiative. A Multidisciplinary study of rapid climate change and future sea level.
20 See Ref 16, Question 4.
21 Met Office, Catarina hits Brazil – South Atlantic Hurricane breaks all the rules.
22 Interdecadal variation in the extent of South Pacific tropical waters during the Younger Dryas event. Thierry Corrège et al. *Nature* 2004, 428, pp 927-929.
23 See Ref 10.
24 *History of the World.* J.M. Roberts. Penguin Books. Third Editon, 1997.
25 Ibid.
26 Ibid
27 Ibid.
28 Abrupt Climate Change. R.B. Alley et al. *Science*, Vol 299 pp2005-2010. 28 March 2003.
29 See Ref 10.
30 See Ref 16, Question3.
31 See Ref 4.
32 Global Warming: The imperatives for action from the science of climate change. Sir David King, Chief Scientific Adviser to the UK Government. Plenary address to the American Association for the Advancement of Science, Seattle, Washington. 13 February 2004.
33 Tony Blair, speaking at the launch of the Climate Group, London, UK. 28 April 2004. www.number-10.gov.uk/output/Page5717.asp
34 Change Science: Adapt, Mitigate, or Ignore? David A. King. *Science*, Vol 3030 pp176-177. 9 Jan 2004
35 See Ref 2

■ The above information is from Friends of the Earth's website: www.foe.co.uk

© *Friends of the Earth*

Climate change heralds thirsty times ahead

Fresh water will be in ever shorter supply as climate change gathers pace. A that increasing temperatures will dramatically affect the world's great rivers.

While flows will increase over-all, with some rivers becoming more swollen, many that provide water for the majority of the world's people will begin to dry up.

Some of these predicted changes are already happening. A second study shows temperature changes have affected the flow in many of the world's 200 largest rivers over the past century, with the flow of Africa's rivers declining over the past 10 years.

Veteran climate modeller Syukuro Manabe and colleagues at Princeton University modelled what effect a quadrupling of atmospheric carbon dioxide above pre-industrial levels would have on the global hydrological cycle over the next 300 years. That looks further ahead than most climate models, but the scenario is inevitable unless governments take drastic action to limit greenhouse gas emissions.

Evaporation and precipitation

Rising CO_2 levels will trigger higher temperatures not only at the Earth's surface, but also in the troposphere, the team says. By factoring this into the models, together with changes to levels of water vapour, cloud cover, solar radiation and ozone, the team predicted the effect that climate change would have on evaporation and precipitation.

Both would increase, the researchers found, causing the discharge of fresh water from rivers around the world to rise by almost 15 per cent. However, while water is going to be more plentiful in regions that already have plenty, the net effect will be to take the world's water further from where the people are.

'Water stresses will increase significantly in regions that are already relatively dry,' Manabe reports in the journal *Climate Change* (vol 64, p 59).

Evaporation will reduce the moisture content of soils in many semi-arid parts of the world, including north-east China, the grasslands of Africa, the Mediterranean and the southern and western coasts of Australia. Soil moisture will fall by up to 40 per cent in southern states of the US, Manabe says.

While flows will increase over-all, with some rivers becoming more swollen, many that provide water for the majority of the world's people will begin to dry up

---

Desert irrigation

The effects on the world's rivers will be just as dramatic. The biggest increases will be in the thinly populated tropics and the far north of Canada and Russia. For instance, the flow of the river Ob in Siberia is projected to increase by 42 per cent by the end of the 23rd century.

This prediction could encourage Russia's plans to divert Siberian rivers to irrigate the deserts around the Aral Sea (*New Scientist*, 9 February 2004).

Similar changes could increase pressure from the US for Canada to allow transfers from its giant Pacific rivers to water the American West. Manabe predicts a 47 per cent increase in the flow of the Yukon river.

By contrast, there will be lower flows in many mid-latitude rivers which run through heavily populated regions. Those that will start to decline include the Mississippi, Mekong and especially the Nile, one of the world's most heavily used and politically contested rivers, where his model predicts an 18 per cent fall in flow.

'Profound challenge'

The changes will present a 'profound challenge' to the world's water managers, Manabe says. They are also likely to fuel calls for a new generation of super-dams and canals to move water round the planet, like China's current scheme to transfer water between north and south.

Some of the findings are controversial. The UK Met Office's climate model predicts that flows in the Amazon could fall this century, while Manabe's team predicts greater rainfall could increase its flow by 23 per cent.

And while Manabe foresees a 49 per cent increase in the flow of the Ganges and Brahmaputra rivers that drain the Himalayas, an international study reported that the Ganges would lose flow as the glaciers that feed it melt away (*New Scientist* print edition, 8 May 2004).

Time delay

Meanwhile, a team of researchers in France say that climate change is already affecting the world's rivers. David Labat and colleagues at the government's CNRS research agency in Toulouse reconstructed the monthly discharges of more than 200 of the world's largest rivers since 1875.

They took discharge data held by the Global Runoff Data Centre in Germany and the UNESCO River Discharge Database and used a statistical technique to fill in gaps left by missing data, or changes to run-off caused by dams and irrigation projects (*Advances in Water Resources*, DOI: 10.1016/j.advwatres.2004.02.020).

Their findings reveal that changing temperatures cause river flows to rise and fall after a delay of

---

The UK Met Office's climate model predicts that flows in the Amazon could fall this century

---

about 15 years, and the team predicts that global flows will increase by about 4 per cent for every 1 °C rise in global temperature.

However, climate change over the past few decades has already caused discharge from rivers in North and South America and Asia to increase. Run-off in Europe has remained stable, but the flow of water from Africa's rivers has fallen.

■ The above information is from the *New Scientist*'s website: www.newscientist.com
© *Reed Business Information Ltd.*

Endangered species

Climate change threatens a million species with extinction

Climate change may drive a quarter of land animals and plants extinct, according to a major new study published in the journal *Nature* – unless greenhouse gas emissions are drastically reduced. The largest collaboration of scientists ever to apply themselves to this problem studied six biodiversity-rich regions around the world representing 20% of the planet's land area. They projected the future distributions of 1,103 plants, mammals, birds, reptiles, frogs, butterflies and other invertebrates. The study employed computer models to simulate the ways species' ranges are expected to move in response to changing temperatures and climatic conditions. The results found that 15 to 37% of all species in the regions considered could be driven extinct from the climate change that is likely to occur between now and 2050.

'If the projections can be extrapolated globally, and to other groups of land animals and plants, our analyses suggest that well over a million species could be threatened with extinction as a result of climate change,' said lead author Chris Thomas of the University of Leeds.

'This study makes clear that climate change is the biggest new extinction threat,' said co-author Lee Hannah, at Conservation International (CI) in Washington DC. 'The combination of increasing habitat loss and climate change together is particularly worrying.

Increases in temperature can force a species to move toward its preferred, usually cooler, climate range. If habitat destruction has already altered those habitats, the species will have no safe haven.'

'In some cases we found that there will no longer be anywhere climatically suitable for these species to live; in other cases they may be unable to reach distant regions where the climate will be suitable,' said co-author Guy Midgley of the National Botanical Institute in Cape Town, South Africa.

'This study makes clear that climate change is the biggest new extinction threat'

In the UK the species with the most uncertain future is the Scottish crossbill, a species of finch confined to the Caledonian pine forest of Highland Scotland. The precise climatic conditions it lives in now may not be found in the UK in the future.

Dr Rhys Green, an RSPB and Cambridge University research scientist and another of the *Nature* paper's co-authors, said: 'It is expected that the climate in the present range in the Scottish Highlands will have changed substantially by the end of this century. Climate similar to that the Scottish crossbill currently occupies will then be found only in Iceland. It seems unlikely that Scottish crossbills will move there, but if they do not, then they will need to adapt to conditions they have not recently experienced.'

Commenting on predicted changes to other birds' ranges, Dr Green added: 'The woodlark and cirl bunting, birds more or less confined in Britain to southern England, are likely to extend their ranges northward, at least into the Midlands and Yorkshire if these warmth-loving birds can exploit suitable climatic conditions further north. Whether they can do so will depend on whether suitable habitats are maintained or created on farmland, areas of forestry and nature reserves.'

The recent rise in global temperature is attributable to human induced activities that have altered the chemical composition of the atmosphere.

Chris Thomas added: 'An immediate and progressive switch to technologies that produce little or no new greenhouse gases, combined with active removal of carbon dioxide from the atmosphere, could save a million or more species from extinction.'

■ The above information is from NFU Countryside's website: www.nfucountryside.org.uk
© *NFU Countryside*

Warmer weather, death, disease and destruction

By Corin Williams

Are we being complacent about the risks we face from global warming? A government report published in 2002 said that thousands could die as a direct result of a warmer climate and that it could cost local authorities and the NHS billions.

Soaring temperatures last summer killed an estimated 2,045 people in England, and 35,000 in Europe as a whole, but the UK climate impact programme predicts more virulent and widespread disease, an extra 10,000 cases of food poisoning, a major increase in skin cancer, and increased respiratory problems from dust, air pollution, gales and floods.

Former environment minister Michael Meacher has plenty to say on the subject. He told EHN: 'The threat we face from the effects of health on climate change is worse than that from terrorism. Many more people will die from climate change. Of the 10 hottest recorded summers of all time, eight of them have been in the last decade. I do not believe this is a coincidence.'

Mr Meacher is not alone in his belief. Sir David King, the prime minister's chief scientist, has been outspoken on US environmental policy and, it is claimed, has been told by the UK government to tone down his criticisms.

In July 2003, Defra published a 'local adaptation guide' for local authorities to help prepare communities for the expected impact of global warming. The guide offers such advice as to 'hose down streets in urban areas' to keep down levels of dust and allergens and to 'provide more shade in public areas'.

> *'The threat we face from the effects of health on climate change is worse than that from terrorism. Many more people will die from climate change.'*

Candice Collier, the UK's first fulltime climate change officer (EHN, 9 January, page 2), thinks the message isn't getting through. 'The Defra report isn't a fantastic document. I'm not sure that the government is fully geared up to getting the issues across. I can't say that health is the top priority in our strategy at the moment, but we are trying to promote more public awareness.

'I don't agree that climate change poses more of a threat than terrorism at all. Often you get a big spin on something people aren't sure about to put the frighteners on.'

Ms Collier echoes a more widespread scepticism: 'It's very difficult to assess the risk. There are lots of scientists out there and for every one theory there will be a conflicting theory.' However, it seems that a broad consensus is forming within the scientific community and the debate is getting more sophisticated.

So will Mr Meacher be stocking up on extra strong suncream and malaria tablets? He says: 'We are in a transitionary period but I suspect that, in 20 to 30 years' time, this will be a serious question. I think it will come. It is estimated that, by 2080, the Greek islands won't be in-habitable – at least, not during the day – no matter how strong your sunblock. Here in Britain we are not remote from such problems – it would be extraordinarily foolish to ignore the threat now.'

■ The above information is from EHN's website which can be found at www.ehn-online.com

Global warming 'will leave Arctic ice-free'

By Jamie Wilson

Global warming is causing the Arctic ice-cap to melt at such an unprecedented rate that by the summer of 2070 it may have no ice at all, according to the most comprehensive study carried out on global climate change in the region.

The ice-cap has shrunk by 15% to 20% in the past 30 years and the trend is set to accelerate, with the Arctic warming almost twice as fast as the rest of the planet, due to a build-up of heat-trapping gases.

The report found that the changes are likely to harm native communities, wildlife and economic activity, but also highlighted some controversial short-term advantages: oil and gas deposits will be easier to reach, more farming may be possible and shortcut trans-Arctic shipping lanes may open, shortening the sea journey between the UK and Japan by up to 12 days.

The findings support the broad scientific consensus that global warming is caused mainly by rising atmospheric greenhouse gases as a result of emissions from cars, factories and power plants.

Conducted by nearly 300 scientists, as well as elders from the native communities in the region, the report was commissioned in 2004 by the eight countries with Arctic territories – including the US – amid a growing sense of urgency about the effects of global warming on the region.

The report says that 'while some historical changes in climate have resulted from natural causes and variations, the strength of the trends and the patterns of change that have emerged indicate that human influences, resulting primarily from increased emissions of carbon dioxide and other greenhouse gases, have now become the dominant factor'.

> **The ice-cap has shrunk by 15% to 20% in the past 30 years and the trend is set to accelerate**

The Arctic 'is now experiencing some of the most rapid and severe climate change on Earth', the report says, adding: 'Over the next 100 years climate change is expected to accelerate, contributing to major physical, ecological, social and economic changes, many of which have already begun.'

Examples include Inuit hunters falling through previously stable ice, permafrost thawing and destabilising foundations of buildings, and the habitat of creatures from polar bears to seals melting away.

'We are taking a risk with the global climate,' said Paal Prestrud, vice-chairman of the Arctic Climate Impact Assessment report.

The WWF environmental group accused the eight nations – which account for 30% of global greenhouse gas emissions – of hypocrisy in sponsoring the report while failing to take action.

'The big melt has begun,' Jennifer Morgan, director of the WWF's global climate change campaign, said in a statement. 'Life on Earth will change beyond recognition with the loss of the ice sheet at the north pole and higher sea levels threatening major global cities such as London.'

George Bush pulled out of the UN's Kyoto protocol on global warming in 2001, arguing it was too expensive.

The other Arctic nations have agreed to Kyoto's emission control target.

© Guardian Newspapers Limited 2004

Climate change and Europe

Europe needs adaptation strategies to limit climate change impacts

More frequent and more economically costly storms, floods, droughts and other extreme weather. Wetter conditions in northern Europe but drier weather in the south that could threaten agriculture in some areas. More frequent and more intense heatwaves, posing a lethal threat to the elderly and frail. Melting glaciers, with three-quarters of those in the Swiss Alps likely to disappear by 2050. Rising sea levels for centuries to come.

These are among the impacts of global climate change that are already being seen in Europe or are projected to happen over the coming decades as global temperatures rise, according to a new report from the European Environment Agency (EEA).

Strong evidence exists that most of the global warming over the past 50 years has been caused by human activities, in particular emissions of heat-trapping greenhouse gases, such as carbon dioxide (CO_2) from the burning of fossil fuels.

The concentration of CO_2, the main greenhouse gas, in the lower atmosphere is now at its highest for at least 420,000 years – possibly even 20 million years – and stands 34% above its level before the Industrial Revolution. The rise has been accelerating since 1950.

The summer floods of 2002 and last year's summer heatwave are recent examples of how destructive extreme weather can be.

The serious flooding in 11 countries in August 2002 killed about 80 people, affected more than 600,000 and caused economic losses of at least 15 billion US$. In the summer 2003 heatwave western and southern Europe recorded more than 20,000 excess deaths, particularly among elderly people. Crop harvests in many southern countries were down by as much as 30%. Melting reduced the mass of the Alpine glaciers by one-tenth in 2003 alone.

'This report pulls together a wealth of evidence that climate change is already happening and having widespread impacts, many of them with substantial economic costs, on people and ecosystems across Europe,' said Prof. Jacqueline McGlade, EEA Executive Director.

She added: 'Europe has to continue to lead worldwide efforts to reduce greenhouse gas emissions, but this report also underlines that strategies are needed, at European, regional, national and local level, to adapt to climate change. This is a phenomenon that will considerably affect our societies and environments for decades and centuries to come.'

The concentration of CO_2, the main greenhouse gas, in the lower atmosphere is now at its highest for at least 420,000 years

---

The extent and rate of the climate changes under way most likely exceed all natural variation in climate over the last thousand years and possibly longer. The 1990s were the warmest decade on record and the three hottest years recorded – 1998, 2002 and 2003 – have occurred in the last six years. The global warming rate is now almost 0.2°C per decade.

Europe is warming faster than the global average. The temperature in Europe has risen by an average of 0.95°C in the last hundred years and is projected to climb by a further 2.0-6.3°C this century as emissions of greenhouse gases continue building up.

As a first step towards reversing this trend, the world's governments in 1997 agreed the Kyoto Protocol, an international treaty under which industrialised countries would reduce their emissions of six greenhouse gases by around 5% between 1990 and 2012.

So far 123 countries, including all member states of the European Union, have ratified the treaty but the US, the biggest emitter of greenhouse gases, has decided against doing so.

In addition to those mentioned above, a broad range of current and future impacts of climate change in Europe are highlighted in the report, including the following:

- Almost two out of every three catastrophic events since 1980 have been directly attributable to floods, storms, droughts or heatwaves. The average number of such weather and climate-related disasters per year doubled over the 1990s compared with the previous decade. Economic losses from such events have more than doubled over the past 20 years to around 11 billion US$ annually. This is due to several reasons, including the greater frequency of such events but also socio-economic factors such as increased household wealth, more urbanisation and more costly infrastructure in vulnerable areas.

- The annual number of floods in Europe and the numbers of people affected by them are rising. Climate change is likely to increase the frequency of flooding, particularly of flash floods, which pose the greatest danger to people.

- Climate change over the past three decades has caused decreases in populations of plant species in various parts of Europe, including mountain regions. Some plants are likely to become extinct as other factors, such as fragmentation of habitats, limit the ability of plant species to adapt to climate change.
- Glaciers in eight of Europe's nine glacial regions are in retreat, and are at their lowest levels for 5,000 years.
- Sea levels in Europe rose by 0.8-3.0 mm per year in the last century. The rate of increase is projected to be 2-4 times higher during this century.
- Projections show that by 2080 cold winters could disappear almost entirely and hot summers, droughts and incidents of heavy rain or hail could become much more frequent.

Climate change does appear to have some positive impacts too, however.

- Agriculture in most parts of Europe, particularly the mid latitudes and northern Europe, could potentially benefit from a limited temperature rise. But while Europe's cultivated area may expand northwards, in some parts of southern Europe agriculture could be threatened by water shortages. And more frequent extreme weather, especially heatwaves, could mean more bad harvests. Whether positive impacts occur will greatly depend on agriculture's capacity to adapt to climate change.
- The annual growing season for plants, including agricultural crops, lengthened by an average of 10 days between 1962 and 1995 and is projected to continue getting longer.
- The survival rate of bird species wintering in Europe has improved over the past few decades and is likely to increase further as winter temperatures continue rising.

The report, *Impacts of climate change in Europe: An indicator-based assessment*, is available at http://reports.eea.eu.int/climate_report_2_2004/en

About the EEA

The European Environment Agency is the leading public body in Europe dedicated to providing sound, independent information on the environment to policy-makers and the public. Operational in Copenhagen since 1994, the EEA is the hub of the European environment information and observation network (Eionet), a network of around 300 bodies across Europe through which it collects and disseminates environment-related data and information. An EU body, the Agency is open to all nations that share its objectives. It currently has 31 member countries: the 25 EU Member States, three EU candidate countries – Bulgaria, Romania and Turkey – and Iceland, Liechtenstein and Norway. A membership agreement has been initialled with Switzerland.

- The above information is from the European Environment Agency's website which can be found at www.eea.eu.int

© European Environment Agency

2050: a fictional vision of the future

Information from the Energy Saving Trust

By the 2050s, the UK could have a climate more like what we currently expect to see in parts of Southern Europe. Water will remain a big issue. Water efficiency measures will help, but drier summers will mean water supplies in the South and East of England will need to be piped in from other regions. New water storage built closer to population centres might also be in place. In the driest years, water for agricultural and industrial use may also be restricted. Garden lawns will be made up from new seed mixes better able to withstand the drier summers and wetter winters, or gardeners may have to switch to something entirely different. Gardeners are likely to have to

Energy Saving Trust

become adept at greywater recycling and rainwater storage as a way to keep their plants irrigated during dry summers. The changing weather patterns could exacerbate subsidence problems in clay soil areas, including the Thames Valley, Bristol and Birmingham, costing some £600 million per year in claims.

Buildings might suffer if wind speeds increase, with perhaps one million properties damaged by the worst storms. Flooding is a potential problem as winter rains grow heavier and sea levels rise. Flood and sea defences will need to protect over two million houses and the 40 per cent of industry that lie near to coasts or river estuaries: that is equivalent to £200 billion of assets. In particular, investment will be needed to protect London and other key places from flooding as well as vulnerable installations such as nuclear power stations, even after they have closed down. Within 50 years from now, significant parts of East Anglia will have to be heavily defended against rising seas, including ports like Felixstowe. Some land could be returned to the sea, called managed retreat, as has already happened at Paull Holme Strays.

Home insurance costs could go through the roof, or perhaps be withdrawn altogether in some places, with annual insurance claims reaching the £800 million mark. Insurers could suffer massively with increased claims for flooding, storm damage and weather disasters worldwide, sending the insurance industry into turmoil.

There are mixed blessings for public health. Milder winters should reduce the number of cold-related deaths, but any serious summer heatwaves could see an increase in heat-related deaths. The heat will also require more careful food handling to avoid rises in food poisoning. Unless we clean up our car exhaust emissions, air pollution will cause bigger health problems in the warmer, sunnier conditions. We will also have to remember to apply plenty of sunscreen throughout the summer to minimise the risk of sunburn and skin cancer.

Heatwaves could create huge demand for air conditioning. Natural ventilation and shading should help minimise this, but power generators will need to plan carefully for changing seasonal demands.

Without action to make the transport infrastructure more climate robust, it could grind to a halt as rails buckle and foundations subside in hot summer while rain and flooding lead to landslides. UK tourism may win as more people shun unbearable summer heat on the Mediterranean for sunshine in the UK, but the ski industry in Scotland will have long since diversified into other forms of tourism as snowfall becomes increasingly rare.

The countryside could be painted with new colours as exotic crops more often grown in Southern Europe will spread northwards, such as maize and sunflowers. The long hot summers will have the potential to boost the British wine industry. The milder winters, however, could encourage pests, diseases and weeds – including new alien invaders which can survive when there are no longer any winter frosts – so farmers will need to be vigilant, introducing new control methods.

Warmer seas around the UK may attract increasing numbers of

On the way in

1. Creepy crawlies
Bloodsucking ticks, scorpions and poisonous spiders all might become a feature of life in a hotter UK

2. Hayfever
Hayfever could be experienced for months on end as trees and grasses flower far beyond their previous seasons

3. Clogged waterways
Once winter frosts disappear, we could see the spread of Water Hyacinth, a vigorous alien weed, which could clog our waterways

4. Pest control
We will need to take action to control infestations of flea, wasp, mice and rat populations, which thrive in the mild winters and hot summers

5. Sharks
Different types of sharks could be spotted off the coast of Scotland and stingrays along the south coast of England in the warmer waters

6. Wisteria scale
We could see a bout of new garden pests such as the Wisteria scale, which could threaten Wisteria plants

7. Termites
These six-legged pests are spreading north through Europe and are already in France, and could reach the UK

8. Vineyards
The North East of Scotland could become warm and dry enough to make a decent white wine

9. Diseases
Mosquitoes carrying diseases such as Dengue fever and West Nile virus have already invaded the US because of rising temperatures. They could become a regular feature in the UK in the future

10. Cleaner air
If we tackle those exhaust emissions we will all be able to breathe more easily

On the way out

1. Scotland's ski resorts
With increasingly mild temperatures and much less snow, Scotland's ski industry has already had to diversify into other activities like mountain biking and paragliding

2. Golf courses
Golf courses could become very expensive to maintain in the long, hot summers with drought and tough water restrictions affecting the quality of grass, and waterlogged conditions in winter

3. The Snowdon lily
The rare Snowdon lily and many other British alpine plants could become extinct, as their mountain homes grow too hot and they face competition from other species

4. Cod
Warm waters further threaten our already dwindling numbers of cod, with cod and chips potentially relegated to a thing of the past

5. The dormouse
The dormouse could disappear as warmer summers and milder winters threaten its habitat

6. The village green
Traditional greens could become difficult to maintain, as soaring temperatures, drought and water restrictions turn them brown, prompting a move to new grass seed mixes

7. Sunbathing
Days spent lying in the sun on a beach could become a thing of the past as holiday makers are more cautious of the summer sun

8. Daffodils
Warmer winter temperatures will put our daffs and crocuses at risk, while other climate change impacts will affect snowdrops, rhododendrons and primula

9. Golden beaches
A trip to the seaside could be a thing of the past, as some sandy beaches are submerged under the rising seas. 70 per cent of the world's sandy shores have already been in retreat over the last century

10. Christmas trees
Spruce tree plantations could die, as they no longer have sufficient cold spells in the winter to allow them to grow the following season

exotic fish, such as mullet and tuna, at the expense of colder-water fish such as cod.

Snapshot of life in 2050
Organisations like EST, UKCIP and others are working together to help ensure that we are prepared for the climate change we can't avoid, and are taking action to stop making climate change even worse. But what might happen if nothing was done to address climate change? Nothing to reduce damaging emissions, nothing to prepare? This is an account of the climate we will avoid by taking action now.

It's another blistering hot day in August. The heatwave has cooked up a thick brown smog, not helped by moorland fires raging out of control and the dust blown from the dry arable fields. Sleeping is difficult in the hot, sticky nights. Using the air conditioning pushes up summer fuel bills – although winter heating bills aren't so high these days – so it is cheaper to leave windows open and sleep under nets to keep the mosquitoes out. Due to the warmer climate all food has to be kept in the fridge otherwise it goes off very quickly and it's surprisingly easy to pick up food poisoning. No one leaves food lying around anyway, the increased number of household pests such as mice are now active all year round as there are fewer cold snaps to control their numbers. Visits from the pest exterminators might become more commonplace.

Buildings insurance premiums have seen a hike to pay for the storm, flood and subsidence damage, although if you live in a flood-zone you're lucky to get any cover at all. Water is a more precious commodity, with no more power showers and restrictions on car washing and garden watering. At least it will be a good year for homegrown Sussex baked beans and Kent olive oil. Traditional cod and chips is now a special treat, but North Sea tuna is surprisingly plentiful even if the potato harvest is vulnerable to dry summers.

Those warmer seas mean that a hot holiday on the South Coast is now as good as the Costa Brava used

to be last century – but the cost of property on the Coast has tripled in value as a result!

An alternative future
It's a great temptation to throw up your hands in defeat and say, 'it's inevitable'. But it doesn't have to be that way.

Picture this scene in the year 2050. It's a cold and dark winter's morning. You get up and switch on the light, powered by energy stored from solar electric cells and the mini-wind turbine on the roof. The central heating comes on, using an energy efficient 'A' rated condensing boiler and heat pump, which turns waste heat into electrical power.

The house soon becomes warm and snug, thanks also to the triple glazed windows fitted with special heat-insulating glass, draught-proof automatic doors, and thick insulation in the walls and roof.

The tiny amount of heat which leaks out into the outside world will be picked up on a satellite in space, monitoring any waste heat from homes, offices and factories. If you leak too much heat it sends a message to the local energy office and they'll send you a bill for harming the environment.

It's a great temptation to throw up your hands in defeat and say, 'it's inevitable'. But it doesn't have to be that way

---

A computer chip in your kettle will buzz a warning if you overfill it and waste electricity. You sit down to watch the morning news on a low energy flat-screen TV. You jump in your electric car powered by a fuel cell that runs on methanol, a renewable fuel made from crops. And as for the car itself, it's made of Soya oil! The oil is converted into a strong plastic that never rusts, and when the car is scrapped it can be recycled like compost!

Public transport provides a cheap and easy alternative to the car. A bus or tram gets you to the local station to take a train for the rest of your journey. Mind you, this isn't the clanking train of olden days – the engine is driven by powerful magnets which levitate the train above the track and shoot it along at some 300 mph at a fraction of the cost of electric or diesel engines, which were a waste of energy.

The highest property prices these days are for homes away from rivers and coasts at risk of flooding, and that are equipped with latest features, like shading and natural ventilation, to prevent overheating in the summer.

This picture of an energy efficient future may sound like a fantasy, but it's all possible with today's technology if only we invested in the technology now.

■ The above information is from *Forecasting the Future – Changing climate, changing behaviour*, a publication by the Energy Saving Trust.

© *Energy Saving Trust*

The way forward

Information from WWF-UK

The way forward

Renewable energy

- Renewable energy sources such as hydro, wind, solar and wave power can satisfy our energy needs while contributing zero or negligible CO_2 emissions.
- Using just one renewable technology – offshore wind – could generate enough electricity to meet a quarter of the UK's demand and still leave much of the resource untapped.[4]
- Denmark already gets 20 per cent of its electricity from wind power.[5]
- The wind industry is already a €7bn sector, and could grow to €75bn annually by 2020. It is feasible for wind power to provide 12 per cent of the global electricity demand by 2020.[6]
- 'Europe is not rich in oil, coal or gas, but we have huge wind resources and European companies are world leaders at converting it into energy. Wind power technology is the "Microsoft of Europe" waiting to be unlocked.' – Corin Millais, EWEA Chief Executive.
- In 2002, wind power was again the world's fastest growing energy source.[1]
- We have more wind off our coasts than anywhere else in Europe.[7]
- Energy crops, which are CO_2 neutral, could supply around 10 per cent of UK electricity by 2025 which equates to 9 per cent of current electricity consumption.[8]

Energy efficiency

- The cheapest, cleanest and safest way of addressing all our (energy and environmental) goals is to be more energy-efficient.[2]
- The average household could save around two tonnes of CO_2 a year by making itself energy efficient.[3]

- If every household installed three energy-efficient lightbulbs, enough energy would be saved in a year to supply all street lighting in the UK.[3]
- More than 40 per cent of all heat lost in the average home is through the loft and walls. In fact, the amount of heat lost annually through roofs and walls is enough to heat three million homes for a year.[3]
- If everyone in the UK installed cavity wall insulation we would cut CO_2 emissions by nine million tonnes. That's enough to fill over 51 million double-decker buses.[3]
- CO_2 emissions would be reduced by 0.45 million tonnes (the volume of 2.5 million double-decker buses) if everyone put an insulation jacket on their hot water tank.[3]
- If everyone upgraded their old fridge to an A-rated Energy Efficiency Recommended product, CO_2 emissions would be cut by the equivalent of 47 million double-deckers of carbon dioxide.[3]

For more energy efficiency facts, visit www.saveenergy.co.uk/why/whysave

---

The cheapest, cleanest and safest way of addressing all our goals is to be more energy-efficient

---

- BedZED – the Beddington Zero Energy Development – is an environmentally-friendly, energy-efficient mix of housing and work space in the London Borough of Sutton. BedZED uses only energy generated on-site from renewable sources. It is the first large-scale 'carbon neutral' community in the UK – it adds no CO_2 to the atmosphere.[9] BedZED delivers a 60 per cent reduction in total energy demand and a 90 per cent reduction in heat demand, compared to a typical suburban home.[9]

Footnotes

1. WWF International website July 2003.
2. Energy White Paper, *Our Energy future – creating a low carbon economy* February 2003. Download from www.dti.gov.uk/energy/publications
3. Save Energy, www.saveenergy.co.uk
4. *Sea Wind East. How offshore wind in East Anglia could supply a quarter of UK electricity needs.* A report for Greenpeace by AEA Technology, 2002.
5. Yes2Wind, www.yes2wind.com
6. *Wind Force 12* – the joint European Wind Energy Association (EWEA) and Greenpeace report, May 2003.
7. BWEA, 2002.
8. *New and Renewable Energy: Prospects for the 21st Century – Supporting Analysis*, UK DTI, March 1999.
9. BedZED, www.bedzed.org.uk July 2003.

Further information

To find out more about WWF's work to combat climate change, visit: www.panda.org/climate

- The above information is from WWF-UK's website which can be found at www.wwf-uk.org

Climate change: the human factor

Information from the Energy Saving Trust

The climate changes for all sorts of reasons. Ocean currents shift, volcanoes shower the world in ash. The sun's energy also slightly changes and for the past century it has been unusually active and affected our climate. But for the past 50 years or so, global temperature rises have been largely due to our own CO_2 pollution.

The two gases that are the biggest contributors to man-made climate change are carbon dioxide and methane. Carbon dioxide remains the chief culprit, and at present about seven billion tonnes of carbon are emitted globally into the atmosphere each year, mostly through the combustion of coal, oil and gas for energy. The majority of scientists, involved in the Intergovernmental Panel on Climate Change, agree that the human impact on climate is substantial.

For centuries there was little change in the concentrations of this gas until the dawn of the industrial age, when the concentrations shot up. Today it is at the highest level for the past 440,000 years. There is now so much carbon dioxide in the air that for the past 200 years plants have been growing fewer pores in their leaves to soak up the abundant gas.

In the UK, 28 per cent of all carbon dioxide emissions released into the atmosphere come from the energy that is used to run our homes.

Every household in the UK creates around six tonnes of carbon dioxide every year – approximately the weight of an African bull elephant and enough to fill six hot air balloons ten metres in diameter.

In fact, the average home is responsible for more harmful carbon dioxide emissions than the average car produces every year. The average household could save around £200 a year by taking energy efficiency measures. This is equivalent to a saving of around two tonnes of CO_2 per year. Space and water heating account for more than 80 per cent of energy consumption in the domestic sector – the amount of heat lost in homes annually through roofs and walls is enough to heat around three million homes for a year, or equivalent to about £1 billion a year.

Energy Saving Trust

What you can do: top ten tips for cutting carbon

1. Buy energy efficient appliances
When replacing appliances, consider their energy efficiency rating. Look for the Energy Efficiency Recommended Logo as a guide to help you choose the most suitable product

2. Choose a high efficiency condensing boiler
If your boiler needs to be replaced, then make sure you replace it with a high-efficiency condensing boiler – from April 2005 this will be law. This could save you around a third on your bills – that's over ten per cent more than replacing with a conventional boiler

3. Consider installing cavity wall insulation
If your home is suitable, about three hours of a professional's time will save you money in the long run

4. Get some lofty ideas
Insulating your loft to a depth of at least 25cm is a great way of cutting down heat loss and you can do it yourself

5. Double glazing
This is another great way of cutting down heat loss and it will also stop rattles, draughts and reduce noise pollution

6. Hot water tank insulation
By fitting a jacket on your tank you can reduce heat loss by around 75 per cent

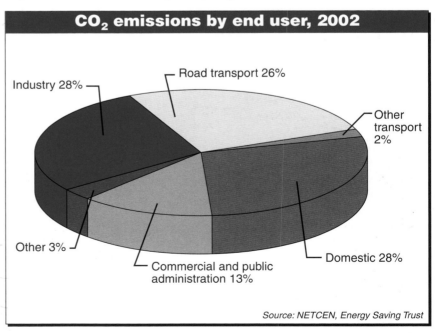

CO₂ emissions by end user, 2002

- Industry 28%
- Road transport 26%
- Other transport 2%
- Domestic 28%
- Commercial and public administration 13%
- Other 3%

Source: NETCEN, Energy Saving Trust

7. Use energy efficient light bulbs
They last up to 12 times longer and use a fraction of the electricity guzzled by ordinary bulbs

8. Turn down the thermostat by one degree
It could cut your heating bills by up to ten per cent

9. Use your car less
Try walking or cycling to the shops occasionally, it's better for you and the environment

10. Think solar
Solar PV panels generate electricity for your home and you could qualify for a grant to contribute to the cost

Energy boosters

- If every household in the UK installed cavity wall insulation (where possible), it would save £670 million a year and nine million tonnes of carbon dioxide annually
- If all homes installed loft insulation up to 25cm thickness, the savings would pay the energy bills of 635,000 families for a year
- If all gas central heating systems used a condensing boiler, it would cut CO_2 emissions by 17.5 million tonnes, saving £1.3 billion on energy bills every year
- Each year, video recorders and televisions consume around £150 million worth of electricity while on standby mode
- If everyone boiled only the water they needed, instead of filling the kettle, it would save enough

If all homes installed loft insulation up to 25cm thickness, the savings would pay the energy bills of 635,000 families for a year

electricity in a year to run more than three-quarters of the street lighting in the entire country

- If every household changed just two ordinary light bulbs for energy efficient ones, enough electricity would be saved each year to power all the street lighting in the UK
- Lowering home heating by just one degree typically saves up to ten per cent of heating costs. If all UK households did this, enough energy would be saved each year to heat nearly 2.8 million homes

Fiscal incentives

Energy efficiency in the home is the key to reducing our impact on the environment. To help households take on board more energy efficiency measures in order to reduce their CO_2 emissions, the EST has called on the Government to introduce a range of fiscal commitments to make this easier and more affordable for households.

In the Energy White Paper, released by the Government in 2002, they made a strong commitment to energy efficiency, describing it as the cheapest, cleanest and safest means of meeting policy objectives. To help achieve this, as part of the Energy Efficiency Commitment (EEC), energy suppliers offer consumers financial reductions on energy efficiency measures such as insulation, condensing boilers, low energy light bulbs and A-rated appliances.

Incentives we have proposed to the Government include:

- An environmental tax or inefficiency charge on the least efficient products
- A proposal to the Chancellor that he should give a rebate on stamp duty to homemovers who install insulation and efficient heating systems when they move to a new home.
- Lowering Council Tax bands for energy efficient homes to give people a financial incentive

We believe these measures would have a positive effect on trade and industry as well as consumers. There are still a lot of smaller things individuals can do to help make a positive difference to the environment. Make sure you turn off your lights when you leave a room, draw your curtains at night and only boil the amount of water you need to make a cup of tea.

■ The above information is an excerpt of *Forecasting the Future – Changing climate, changing behaviour*, a publication produced by the Energy Saving Trust. For further information, visit their website: www.est.org.uk

© Energy Saving Trust

Take the climate challenge and save energy

Information from Friends of the Earth

As Energy Efficiency Week starts,[1] Friends of the Earth is calling on people to pledge to take the Climate Challenge and cut back on the amount of energy they use.

Emissions of carbon dioxide from energy use are contributing to climate change – one of the biggest threats facing the future of the planet.[2] It is clear that world leaders need to take urgent action to tackle the problem but everyone can do something to reduce the impacts of climate change by cutting back on the amount of energy they use.

Friends of the Earth's Climate Challenge – see www.foe.co.uk/climate_challenge or call 0808 800 1111 – starts from easy step solutions to saving energy at home and cutting back on car use, through to tougher steps to reduce your contribution to climate change.

Friends of the Earth's Climate spokesperson, Karine Pellaumail, said:

'Now is the time for people to take action to tackle dangerous climate change, before it's too late. People can start by cutting the energy consumption in their home, reducing their car use or switching to a green electricity provider. Or they could go even further by installing renewable energy in their homes or getting their workplace, local school or hospital to install renewable energy as well.'

Friends of the Earth's Climate Challenge has a scale of difficulty from one to three plus stars. The more stars, the greater the difference made to tackling climate change. For more information, see www.foe.co.uk/climate_challenge

1 star challenges

* Be energy aware: switch to low energy bulbs, fill the kettle with only the water needed, turn the thermostat down by just one degree, take showers rather than baths and

Friends of the Earth

only use a washing-machine on full load.

* Buy green electricity: Friends of the Earth recommends the following tariffs (in alphabetical order): Eco Energy, Ecotricity Old Energy Tariff, Good Energy (previously known as unit[e]), Green Energy 100, RSPB Energy.

2 star challenges

** Cut emissions from transport: take buses, trains or cycle and walk in preference to using cars or planes.
** Improve the energy efficiency of your home: install insulation in your loft or in the cavity of your walls, buy a condensing boiler. The Energy Saving Trust has information on what you can do to improve the energy efficiency of your home, how to get grants and how you may be eligible for reduced prices on installing energy efficiency measures.
** Become an investor in renewable energy: with as little as £250 it is

possible to join a co-operative through Energy4All, and become an investor in wind energy projects.

3 star challenges

*** Green your workplace: get your workplace to switch off electrical equipment when not in use, re-use and recycle paper and packaging, and encourage employees to cycle, share cars and use public transport to go to work.
*** Install your own renewable energy: be a renewable energy pioneer and install renewable energy in your home. Grants are currently available for up to 50% of the capital costs of installing renewable energy to help make it cost effective.
*** Adopt a renewable energy project: have a look at www.Yes2Wind.org, a coalition website which aims to provide information and resources for the public to support wind farms locally. Or find out about other renewable energy projects that are planned in your area by writing a letter to the planning department or local media.
*** Get a local institution or business to install renewable energy: encourage schools, hospitals, universities and businesses to invest in their own on-site renewable energy to meet some of their energy needs.

3 star + challenges

***+ Set up a group climate challenge: pledge a challenging challenge such as getting 50 people to switch to green electricity. You may want to join your local Friends of the Earth group first.

Notes
1 www.est.org.uk/myhome
2 www.foe.co.uk/campaigns/climate

■ The above information is from Friends of the Earth's website which can be found at www.foe.co.uk

© *Friends of the Earth*

And yet it melts

Climate change

Some people still think the world is flat. Others firmly believe that the sun rotates around the earth. In spite of all the evidence to the contrary, they cling to their opinions based on the naive realism of what they can see with their own eyes and nothing else. In children or most adults, such beliefs are quaint or merely cranky at worst. But there is a class of events that too many people, and too many otherwise sensible people in positions of authority, refuse to see: climate change. True, the facts of global warming and its consequences are large, complex, slow-moving and depressing, and addressing it threatens to be expensive and difficult. But the evidence of climate change continues to move heavily towards the need to stop its causes. As with discredited ideas that the earth is at the centre of the universe or is flat, there will always be some who disagree. But climate change deniers, for all their easy scepticism and Popperesque deployment of arguments, cannot be allowed to outweigh the very real evidence that the world is in danger.

The latest profound signs of global warming come from the frozen Arctic. Involving hundreds of scientists and six indigenous communities, the Arctic Climate Impact Assessment draws on a comprehensive survey carried out over four years in the eight countries that abut the North Pole. It reveals a catalogue of evidence that should prompt the most hardened sceptics to think again – especially those who argue that natural causes and variations are being mistaken for human-made climate change. The report, commissioned by the Arctic Council, states baldly that 'human influences, resulting primarily from increased emissions of carbon dioxide and other greenhouse gases, have now become the dominant factor'. The Arctic, it goes on, 'is now experiencing some of the most rapid and severe climate change on earth' – twice as fast as previously estimated.

There are a number of disturbing aspects to this report – not least the accusation by some European researchers involved that its publication was being delayed until after the US election to spare the blushes of the Bush administration. But the report's evidence speaks for itself: the Arctic's icecap is melting at an unprecedented rate, while the giant ice sheets of Greenland are under threat. But the most worrying aspect is the report's suggestion that at the current rate of warming, there may be no ice at all in the Arctic come the summer of 2070 – effectively killing one of the world's most distinctive and rich ecosystems.

> *The Arctic 'is now experiencing some of the most rapid and severe climate change on earth' – twice as fast as previously estimated*

What happens now? Given the weight and scope of evidence, the report's conclusions that rapid efforts to cut greenhouse gas emissions would slow down the pace of climate change must be followed. The international community has an early opportunity to make use of this report, when foreign ministers of the Arctic border nations – including the United States – meet in Iceland later this month. But until the US agrees to re-enter the negotiating process under which the Kyoto protocol was drawn up, there is little to be expected from the world's biggest polluter in making the sorts of cuts that would be required. There are other things that can be done to at least lessen the impact on the Arctic itself, such as cutting back on overfishing in the region – one of the factors that 'threaten to overwhelm the adaptive capacity' of the Arctic's environment. In more direct terms, there are high hopes that today's conference in Berlin – being opened by the Queen, another convert to the cause of climate change – will charge the UK with an effective strategy for tackling greenhouse gas emissions. If we take this threat seriously we must face the hard facts that our patterns of energy usage and sources must change. The Arctic may be disappearing, but global warming will not.

© *Guardian Newspapers Limited, November 2004*

Reducing greenhouse gas emissions

Making efficiency pay off

- Getting more electricity, transport, and industrial output for less coal, oil, or gasoline is a no-lose situation: more profit, less pollution, less global warming . . . although initial outlays for better equipment and technology can be expensive.

- Most of the immediate progress that can be made to reduce greenhouse-gas emissions involves using fossil fuels more efficiently. The savings realised this way will buy time for the global climate system while alternative-energy technologies can be developed and made cost-effective. It is hoped that emissions-free sources ultimately will replace fossil fuels as the main category of energy supply.

- 'Combined-cycle' turbines – in which the heat from burning fuel drives steam turbines while the thermal expansion of the exhaust gases drives gas turbines – can boost the efficiency of electricity generation by 70 per cent. In the longer term, new technologies could double the efficiency of power plants.

- Gasoline fuel cells and other advanced automotive technologies can cut carbon-dioxide emissions from transport roughly in half, as can 'hybrid' gas/electricity vehicles, some of which are already on the market.

- Natural gas releases less carbon dioxide per unit of energy than coal or oil. Hence, switching to natural gas is a quick way to cut emissions.

- Industry, which accounts for over 40 per cent of global carbon-dioxide emissions, can benefit from combined heat and power co-generation, other uses of waste heat, improved energy management, and more efficient manufacturing processes.

- Installing more efficient lighting and appliances in buildings can significantly cut electricity use. Improving building insulation can greatly reduce the amount of fuel needed for heating or air conditioning.

Taking advantage of existing renewable energy technologies

- Solar energy and wind-generated electricity – at current levels of efficiency and cost – can replace some fossil-fuel use, and are increasingly being used. Greater employment of such technologies can increase their efficiencies of scale and lower their costs. The current contribution of such energy-producing methods to world supplies is less than 2 per cent.

- Expansion of hydro-electric power, where appropriate, could make a major contribution to lowering greenhouse-gas

emissions . . . but the use of hydropower is necessarily limited by its impacts on human settlements and river systems.

- Biomass sources of energy – such as fuelwood, alcohol fermented from sugar, combustible oils extracted from soybeans, and methane gas emitted by waste dumps – can help cut greenhouse-gas emissions, but only if vegetation used for the purpose is replaced by equal amounts of replanted vegetation (so that the carbon dioxide released by biomass combustion is recaptured through photosynthesis).

- Nuclear energy produces virtually no greenhouse gases, but public concern over safety, transport and disposal of radioactive wastes – not to mention weapons proliferation – means that the responsible employment of nuclear power will likely remain limited. It now accounts for about 6.8 per cent of global energy supplies.

- New technologies have become available for 'capturing' the carbon dioxide emitted by fossil-fuel power plants before it reaches the atmosphere. The carbon dioxide is then stored underground in empty oil or gas reservoirs, unused coal beds, or in the deep ocean. While not exactly 'renewable', this approach, which is already in limited use, is being scrutinised for possible risks and environmental impacts.

- The above information is from the United Nations Framework Convention on Climate Change's website which can be found at www.unfccc.int Alternatively, see page 41 for their address details.

Climate change 'to reverse human progress'

Global warming threatens to reverse human progress and make international targets on halving world poverty by 2015 unattainable, said a study published 20 October 2004.

The claim comes from charities including Greenpeace, Oxfam and Action Aid who joined forces, under the banner of the Working Group on Climate Change and Development, to release the report, called *Up In Smoke*, in London on 20 October 2004.

The group's warning follows a summer in which hurricanes Jeanne and Ivan wreaked havoc across the Caribbean and Bangladesh saw its worst flooding for years.

In a world in which global warming is a reality, it says, such severe weather events are likely to become more frequent and extreme – and the poor will be hardest hit.

The group is urging the international community to take urgent action to introduce:

- A global risk assessment of the likely costs of adaptation to climate change in poor countries
- Cuts in emissions of greenhouse gases by industrialised countries of between 60% and 80%, relative to 1990 levels, by the middle of this century. This goes far beyond the targets of the Kyoto protocol on climate change.

The report says the cuts are vital in order to stop climate change running out of control – defined as a rise in global average temperatures of more than 2°C (4°F) above pre-industrial levels.

- New funding to help poor countries adapt – bearing in mind that rich countries' subsidies to their own fossil fuel industries stood at $73bn (£40bn) a year in the late 1990s.
- Effective and efficient arrangements to respond to the increasing burden of climate-related disaster relief.
- Small-scale renewable energy projects promoted by governments and community groups that can be copied and developed in order to help tackle poverty and reduce climate change.

This move will require political commitment in the form of new funds from governments in all countries and a major shift in priorities by the World Bank and other development bodies, the report says.

- Coordinated local and international plans for relocating threatened communities with appropriate political, legal and financial resources.

In a world in which global warming is a reality, such severe weather events are likely to become more frequent and extreme – and the poor will be hardest hit

---

The report says the prime minister, Tony Blair, has signalled that he will use the UK's presidency of the G8 nations in 2005 to bring the issues of climate change and Africa – where many of the world's poorest countries are found – to the top of the international political agenda.

Welcoming this commitment, the coalition says an either/or approach to climate change and poverty reduction is not an option: the world must face up to the inseparable challenges of poverty and a rapidly warming global climate.

Andrew Simms, author and policy director of the New Economics Foundation, which organised it, said: 'Thousands of people, from the grassroots to Gordon Brown, are aiming to make poverty history, but global warming has been critically overlooked. Like a fire smouldering in the basement it threatens to burn down all they have built up.

'To rescue the situation we need a global framework to stop climate change that is based on equality, and we have to ensure that plans for human development are made both climate proof and climate friendly.'

Archbishop Tutu, Nobel Peace laureate and former Anglican archbishop of Cape Town, said: 'I urge governments and development and environmental organisations to work together to find sustainable solutions to avert a catastrophe that will exacerbate human suffering to a magnitude that perhaps the world has not yet seen.'

The environment secretary, Margaret Beckett, told BBC Radio 4's *Today* programme that Mr Blair would make climate change a priority during Britain's presidency of the G8.

Ms Beckett said: 'No one can welcome what the report says, but . . . I very much welcome the direction of the report and the way that it is bringing people with these concerns together.'

She said she hoped the report would increase pressure on the US to shift its stance on global warming.

'It is true that the present American administration – and the last one – were not prepared to sign up to the Kyoto protocol, but we are moving on without America,' she said.

The environment secretary rejected claims that climate change could only be halted by a switch to nuclear power.

The government has not ruled out the future development of nuclear power, but Ms Beckett made it clear that she did not accept the argument that it was a 'clean' fuel because it did not produce carbon emissions.

© Guardian Newspapers Limited 2004

Delivering change

Margaret Beckett outlines a new initiative to break down barriers to increasing energy efficiency and the use of renewables

A low-carbon economy is attainable. All countries need to have the serious intention to move towards it and thus enhance our collective energy security.

We in the United Kingdom have already taken a major step. In February 2003 we published our Energy White Paper – the United Kingdom's first comprehensive forward-looking statement of energy policy in over 20 years, acknowledging the fundamental interdependence of economic growth, social progress and environmental objectives. A long-term strategy, its key aim is a 60 per cent cut in carbon dioxide emissions by about 2050.

But a global low-carbon economy will not be realised just because the United Kingdom and some like-minded countries wish it. Global participation is essential and governments cannot deliver it alone. Policy makers, business and civil society need to work closely together to deliver the changes we need.

Last year at the Johannesburg World Summit on Sustainable Development, I launched the idea of the Renewable Energy and Energy Efficiency Partnership (REEEP), founded by a group of governments, businesses and non-governmental organisations who felt that partnership was crucial to delivering the sustainable energy commitments we all agreed at the Summit.

I believe it to be a key vehicle for turning such commitments into positive outcomes, harnessing the best ideas from across the globe to achieve just this.

Overcoming barriers

Efficient energy use will be essential. Through the REEEP, our experience and those of many other countries in implementing energy efficiency policies and programmes can benefit all. We in the United Kingdom very much look forward to learning from the experience of others.

By Margaret Beckett

We also need an urgent and substantial increase in the use of renewable energy sources. Through the REEEP we can work together to achieve this.

Barriers to the uptake of renewable and energy efficiency technologies remain: inappropriate policies, subsidies and structural arrangements; problems in accessing finance; and a lack of human and institutional capacity. Overcoming them requires concerted effort from governments, businesses, financial institutions and the rest of civil society. The REEEP can help channel this activity at a regional

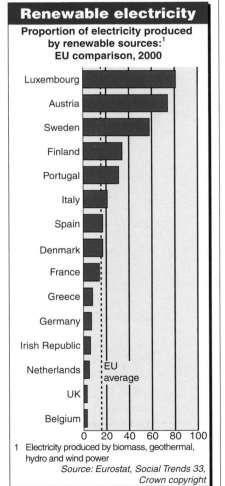

Renewable electricity

Proportion of electricity produced by renewable sources:[1]
EU comparison, 2000

Luxembourg
Austria
Sweden
Finland
Portugal
Italy
Spain
Denmark
France
Greece
Germany
Irish Republic
Netherlands — EU average
UK
Belgium

0 20 40 60 80 100

1 Electricity produced by biomass, geothermal, hydro and wind power

Source: Eurostat, Social Trends 33, Crown copyright

and a global level, ensuring that climate-friendly policies go hand in hand with economic growth, poverty reduction and respect for the varied needs of developing countries.

We need to deliver increased energy efficiency and use of renewable energy. More technological development and international cooperation can help. We need a global partnership of governments, businesses and other stakeholders working together to foster market growth in renewable and energy efficiency technologies and striving to remove policy, technical, market and regulatory barriers to it. Climate-friendly technologies can help create a competitive and sustainable economy, while showing that ambitious and long-term targets on climate change are achievable.

Partners in the REEEP will work in three main areas:

- Identifying and removing market barriers. These will be different depending on location, so the REEEP has an important regional dimension. A network of regulators – or a series of networks – is likely to be one of its early achievements.

- Helping to match finance with innovative renewable and energy efficiency projects. By facilitating links between business and other innovators, REEEP partners will promote sustainable energy projects at the national and regional level – such as the development of energy services markets, tradable renewable energy certificate schemes and the European Union carbon emissions trading scheme.

- Having an important communications role, promoting and explaining the benefits of renewable energy and energy efficiency to international organisations, governments, regulators, business and other key stakeholders.

Opening doors

As a global partnership, the REEEP offers an opportunity to influence the future direction of a new and expanding market and a unique access to key policy makers and regulators. It opens doors to new technology and the opportunity for innovations to be shared globally. It provides the chance to evaluate options against what has worked – and what has not – in different countries and regions.

It has already demonstrated its worth. A regional plan was drawn up at a recent REEEP partners' meeting in Beijing to enable countries to work

together to deliver energy efficiency and increase the use of renewable energy.

A global low-carbon economy is within our grasp. But we need to work together to achieve it, to reduce costs and share knowledge, experience and practice. The REEEP will play a vital role in helping us to get there.

■ Margaret Beckett is Secretary of State for the Environment, Food and Rural Affairs, United Kingdom.

■ This article first appeared in *Our Planet*, Volume 14, the magazine of the United Nations Environment Programme (UNEP). See their websites at www.ourplanet.com and www.unep.org

© United Nations Environment Programme (UNEP)

The international fight against climate change

Blair must put more pressure on USA over climate change

Tony Blair must put intense pressure on George Bush to join the rest of the world in the fight against climate change, Friends of the Earth said 3 November 2004. The US has refused to join international efforts to combat global warming despite being the biggest polluter in the world.

President Bush pulled out of the Kyoto Protocol in 2001, arguing that US business interests would be harmed by the treaty. The United States is responsible for a quarter of the world's carbon dioxide emissions (the principal greenhouse gas), yet it only has around four per cent of the world's population.

The Bush administration exaggerated the scientific uncertainties in order to confuse the case for action. Voluntary US measures to combat global warming have been in place for over ten years, over this period US emissions have increased by 14 per cent. Its Kyoto commitment – which it refuses to ratify – was to reduce them by six per cent.

Friends of the Earth's Director Tony Juniper said: 'The USA is becoming increasingly isolated over climate change. Last month Russia finally ratified the Kyoto Protocol, the international treaty aimed at cutting emissions of the gases responsible for climate change. This crucial decision by Russia means that the Kyoto Protocol will now come into effect early next year.'

And Tony Blair has promised to put climate change at the top of the international agenda at next year's G8 summit, which the UK will host.

The United States is responsible for a quarter of the world's carbon dioxide emissions (the principal greenhouse gas), yet it only has around four per cent of the world's population

---

President Bush has an appalling environmental record.

He has invested some US $38 billion in subsidies to fossil fuel and nuclear industries, advanced policies to open up Africa and Central Asia to oil exploration, and allowing drilling for oil in Alaska.

Friends of the Earth also pointed to his support for genetically modified food and crops, which has resulted in the US making a complaint to the World Trade Organisation (WTO) about European attempts to regulate GM. If the complaint is successful, it could force European states to open their markets to GM produce, regardless of the views of their citizens.

At home, Bush has also come under heavy criticism from environmental organisations for weakening environmental protection legislation, by increasing the levels of emissions allowed under the Clean Air Act and allowing dumping of mining waste in rivers as part of the Clean Water Act. Indeed Bush was described by Dr Brent Blackwelder, President of Friends of the Earth US as 'the most planet-trashing president in US history'.

■ The above information is from Friends of the Earth's website which can be found at www.foe.co.uk

© Friends of the Earth

Global warming's uphill challenge

One month's rainfall in two hours, drought, melting glaciers, lives lost, homes destroyed

Floods in Bangladesh, droughts in sub-Saharan Africa and flash flooding in London – the weather remains a constant talking point.

The 10 hottest years on record in the UK have all occurred since 1990. Last year saw record temperatures across huge swathes of southern England, as the thermometer topped the 100F mark.

Climate change is the most serious long-term threat facing the future of the planet and one that must be addressed globally. It is no longer an issue that can be delayed for another generation – action is needed now.

Global average temperatures rose by 0.6°C during the 20th century, and there is strong evidence that this warming has been caused by increasing concentrations of greenhouse gases – most particularly carbon dioxide – in the atmosphere.

Our continuing use of fossil fuels, whether through the production of electricity or the escalating use of cars and planes, is the primary source of these increasing levels of gases.

Climate change affects the environment that people and wildlife depend on. For example, the heatwave across Europe last year led to about 26,000 early deaths. In the Arctic, indigenous people are already reporting that thinning and depletion of sea-ice in the Arctic could 'push to extinction' key marine mammals including polar bear, walrus and some species of seal hunted by Inuit. In turn this may threaten the existence of Inuit as a hunting culture.

Our chairmanship of the G8 Presidency, which begins in January 2005, and the EU Presidency later in the year, provide the UK with a vital chance to push climate change up the international agenda.

The UK will be using this chance to work with the leading economies of the world to demonstrate that taking action on climate change is not an unbearable burden. By sending a strong signal to the markets that action on climate change is inevitable, we will encourage them to respond.

Low-carbon alternatives will be needed if we are to make the cuts of some 60 per cent in global emissions which scientists say are necessary to avoid dangerous climate change.

Progress is being made. The Kyoto Protocol, which has set developed countries to reduce their overall emissions of greenhouse gases, has now been ratified by 124 countries, although sadly not by the United States or Australia.

The UK Government has agreed to reduce its emissions to 12.5 per cent below 1990 levels and is on track to do so. Through our Climate Change Programme, which is being reviewed later this Autumn, we have introduced a programme of policies and measures to reduce the country's own greenhouse gas emissions.

The UK has introduced a climate change levy on energy use in business and the public sector, which is helping fund measures to promote better energy efficiency.

The climate change agreements will give a discount on the levy rate

---

Our continuing use of fossil fuels, whether through the production of electricity or the escalating use of cars and planes, is the primary source of these increasing levels of gases

---

for those energy intensive sectors of industry that have agreed to meet challenging targets for improving energy efficiency or reducing greenhouse gas emissions. In the residential sector, energy suppliers are obliged to meet targets to improve household energy efficiency.

The UK has introduced an economy wide emissions trading scheme and an obligation on energy suppliers to generate 10 per cent of electricity from renewables by 2010. And we have an aspiration to double this to 20 per cent by 2020.

Through the Energy White Paper, the UK aims to reduce carbon dioxide emissions by 60 per cent by 2050 – necessary to tackle climate change in the medium term.

In addition to tackling the emissions which cause climate change, preparing for the impacts is vital. Government is incorporating a climate change perspective into many major policy areas, and is encouraging other public and private sector organisations to do the same.

But while the Government has a vital role to play in raising awareness, the core objective of combating climate change needs to be a shared one. Five simple things can help reduce greenhouse gas emissions:

- walk or cycle to work each day
- buy local food rather than food that has been transported by air for thousands of miles
- turn off televisions, computers and lights when not needed
- share lifts with friends when travelling by car
- use public transport more.

■ The above information is from the Department for Environment, Food and Rural Affairs' website: www.defra.gov.uk

© *Department for Environment, Food and Rural Affairs (DEFRA)*

Kyoto saved: not yet the planet

Information from Greenpeace

The Russian parliament voted to ratify the Kyoto Protocol on 22 October 2004 in a blow to George W. Bush's opposition to action on climate change.

Kyoto coming in to force is a geopolitical ground shift. Russian ratification pushes this global climate protection agreement over the threshold required to become international law.

You can feel the tectonic plates of global politics grating on one another as the rest of the world signs up to the Protocol and leaves the Bush administration and their largest single share of the globe's greenhouse gas emissions behind.

We can only hope that the industrial revolution of the 20th century will be followed by an energy revolution of equal magnitude in the 21st.

The goal of the international climate regime is to 'avoid dangerous climate change'. Unfortunately, 'dangerous' is in the eye of the beholder, or the victim. To Pacific islanders whose homes are vanishing beneath the waves, to Arctic indigenous people whose way of life is being erased due to climate change already, we have already crossed that threshold. The same could be said for devastated homeowners in the Caribbean, Florida and the recent victims of typhoons in Japan. The tens of thousands of people who died in the summer heat waves in Europe two years ago also probably thought it was a bit 'dangerous'.

What's another two degrees?

Scientists have drawn a line in the sand: a point at which the impacts of climate change become not just bad, but calamitous and in some cases irreversible.

They benchmark it at '2°C global average temperature increase above pre-industrial levels'. If we

turned off the smokestacks today the greenhouse gases already loaded into the atmosphere would take us to 1.3°C.

If global temperatures hit that barrier, it's bad news for all of us. It raises the likelihood of the complete meltdown of the Greenland ice sheet, and possible collapse of the Amazon rainforest ecosystem. Tens of millions of people could suddenly be hungry, hundreds of millions would find themselves threatened with malaria in places where malaria had never previously occurred, millions could have their homes flooded and billions could be without enough water.

'Already we are witnessing increased storms at sea and floods in our cities,' Chief UK Scientist David King said recently. 'Global warming will increase the level and frequency at which we experience heightened weather patterns.'

Now that we have the Protocol in place, the only question that remains is whether politicians can act faster than climate can change

'Kyoto is not enough, Kyoto is a beginning and it's a good process,' he told the third Greenpeace Business lecture in London last week. 'And what will be needed is once we've got the process up and running, it will need to be ratcheted up so that we can really bring emissions under control.'

We believe that the world needs to bring total emissions back to 1990 levels by about 2020, then reduce them by 50 per cent by mid-century. But even that may be too conservative a strategy if the recent unexplained spikes in carbon dioxide emissions continue for the next few years on trend. Now that we have the Protocol in place, the only question that remains is whether politicians can act faster than climate can change.

Take action

Fortunately, some in the US are breaking ranks with the Bush administration's opposition to the treaty and Esso's corporate strategy of active lobbying to undermine it. Join them by boycotting Esso. Don't buy Esso.

■ The above information is from Greenpeace's website which can be found at www.greenpeace.org.uk

© Greenpeace

■ Climate change is likely to have a significant impact on the global environment. In general, the faster the climate changes, the greater will be the risk of damage. (p. 1)

■ The main greenhouse gases are water vapour, carbon dioxide, ozone, methane, nitrous oxide, and the chlorfluorcarbons (CFCs). (p. 1)

■ Most of the energy available on Earth comes from the Sun. It arrives as radiation (heat, light, radiowaves). In just one second the Earth receives more energy than all the electricity used in the UK in a whole month! (p. 2)

■ Though the average global temperature may rise, this single figure may not tell the whole story. For example, it does not mean that they will go up everywhere or for the whole year. As a result of global warming, the UK may actually become colder! (p. 3)

■ If no action is taken the greenhouse effect could lead to a rise in average global temperatures of between 1.5-4.5 degrees Celcius as early as the year 2030. (p. 5)

■ Carbon dioxide levels in the atmosphere have increased from about 280ppm (parts per million) in the mid-18th century – the start of the industrial revolution – to around 379ppm today. You would need to go back millions of years to find such high levels of carbon dioxide in the atmosphere. Methane levels in the atmosphere more than doubled in the last century. (p. 6)

■ This rate of warming is much larger than experienced during the 20th century and is very likely to be unprecedented in the last 10,000 years. (p. 6)

■ The greenhouse gases already emitted since the industrial revolution have committed us to a temperature rise of a degree or so. (p. 8)

■ Global warming is a 'modern' problem – complicated, involving the entire world, tangled up with difficult issues such as poverty, economic development, and population growth. Dealing with it will not be easy. Ignoring it will be worse. (p. 9)

■ Rising global temperature means more than just extra time to wear shorts and sandals. An increase of just a few degrees in average temperature can cause dramatic changes in conditions that are important to the quality of life – and even the Earth's ability to support life. (p. 11)

■ We must not be forced to choose between economic catastrophe and climate catastrophe . . . the most likely outcome in that case would be both, and we have a good chance of avoiding this if we act now. (p. 13)

■ The temperature of the world's oceans is rising. This rising heat will cause the sea water to expand, raising tide levels, causing coastal flooding especially in low-lying river delta and island areas. It is predicted that this combined with the extra water released from melting glaciers and ice caps will cause a 15-95cm rise in sea levels by 2100 on top of the 10-25cm already experienced. (p. 14)

■ A warming of just 2 to 3°C in the next 100 years would put 3 billion people at risk from water shortage, an extra 300 million facing the threat of malaria and 100 million more in danger because of coastal flooding. (p. 17)

■ Climate change will not only cause changes in average temperatures, but will also trigger more so-called extreme weather events. (p. 19)

■ 'The threat we face from the effects of health on climate change is worse than that from terrorism. Many more people will die from climate change.' (p. 23)

■ The ice-cap has shrunk by 15% to 20% in the past 30 years and the trend is set to accelerate, with the Arctic warming almost twice as fast as the rest of the planet, due to a build-up of heat-trapping gases. (p. 24)

■ Europe is warming faster than the global average. The temperature in Europe has risen by an average of 0.95oC in the last hundred years and is projected to climb by a further 2.0-6.3°C this century as emissions of greenhouse gases continue building up. (p. 25)

■ Flood and sea defences will need to protect over two million houses and the 40 per cent of industry that lie near to coasts or river estuaries: that is equivalent to £200 billion of assets. (p. 26)

■ If every household in the UK installed cavity wall insulation (where possible), it would save £670 million a year and nine million tonnes of carbon dioxide annually. (p. 31)

■ Emissions of carbon dioxide from energy use are contributing to climate change – one of the biggest threats facing the future of the planet.2 It is clear that world leaders need to take urgent action to tackle the problem but everyone can do something to reduce the impacts of climate change by cutting back on the amount of energy they use. (p. 32)

■ In a world in which global warming is a reality, such severe weather events are likely to become more frequent and extreme – and the poor will be hardest hit. (p. 35)

■ We need to deliver increased energy efficiency and use of renewable energy. More technological development and international cooperation can help. We need a global partnership of governments, businesses and other stakeholders working together to foster market growth in renewable and energy efficiency technologies and striving to remove policy, technical, market and regulatory barriers to it. (p. 36)

ADDITIONAL RESOURCES

You might like to contact the following organisations for further information. Due to the increasing cost of postage, many organisations cannot respond to enquiries unless they receive a stamped, addressed envelope.

Climate Action Network Europe
Rue de la Charite, 48
1210, Brussels
Belgium
Tel: +32 (0) 2 229 52 20
Fax: +32 (0) 2 229 52 29
E-mail: info@climnet.org
Website: www.climnet.org

Energy Saving Trust
21 Dartmouth Street
London, SW1H 9BP
Tel: 020 7222 0101
Fax: 020 7654 2444
Website: www.est.org.uk

Environmental Health News
Chadwick House Publishing
Chadwick Court,15 Hatfields
London, SE1 8DJ
Tel: 020 7928 6006
Fax: 020 7827 5866
E-mail: ehn@ehn-online.com
Website: www.ehn-online.com

European Environment Agency
Kongens
Nytorv 6,
DK-1050 Copenhagen K
Tel: + 45 33 36 71 00
Fax: + 45 33 36 71 99
Website: www.eea.eu.int

Friends of the Earth (FOE)
26-28 Underwood Street
London, N1 7JQ
Tel: 020 7490 1555
Fax: 020 7490 0881
E-mail: info@foe.co.uk
Website: www.foe.co.uk
Website: www.foei.org
As an independent environmental group, Friends of the Earth publishes a comprehensive range of leaflets, books and in-depth briefings and reports.

Greenpeace
Canonbury Villas
London, N1 2PN
Tel: 020 7865 8100
Fax: 020 7865 8200
E-mail: gn-info@uk.greenpeace.org
Website: www.greenpeace.org.uk

Natural Environment Research Council (NERC)
Polaris House
North Star Avenue
Swindon
Wiltshire, SN2 1EU
Tel: 01793 411500
Fax: 01793 411501
Website: www.nerc.ac.uk

People & Planet
51 Union Street
Oxford, OX4 1JP
Tel: 01865 245678
Fax: 01865 791927
E-mail:
people@peopleandplanet.org
Website: www.peopleandplanet.org

United Nations Environmental Programme (UNEP)
Division of Communications and Public Information
PO Box 30552
Nairobi
Kenya
Tel: + 254 2 621 234
Fax: + 254 2 623 927
E-mail: cpinfo@unep.org
Website: www.unep.org
www.ourplanet

United Nations Framework Convention on Climate Change (UNFCCC)
Haus Carstanjen
Martin-Luther-King-Strasse 8
D-53175 Bonn
Germany
Tel: + 49 228 815 1000
Fax: + 49 228 815 1999
E-mail: secretariat@unfccc.int
Website: www.unfccc.int

United Utilities PLC
Leigh Environment Education Centre
Hope Carr Terrace
Leigh, W17 3XB
Tel: 01942 604057
Fax: 01942 269028
Website: www.unitedutilities.com

Worldwatch Institute
1776 Massachusetts Ave., N.W.
Washington, DC 20036-1904
USA
Tel: + 1 202 452 1999
Fax: + 1 202 296 7365
E-mail:
worldwatch@worldwatch.org
Website: www.worldwatch.org

WWF-UK
Panda House
Weyside Park
Catteshall Lane
Goldalming
Surrey, GU7 1XR
Tel: 01483 426444
Fax: 01483 426409
Website: www.wwf-uk.org

Young People's Trust for the Environment
8 Leapale Road
Guildford
Surrey, GU1 4JX
Tel: 01483 539600
Fax: 01483 301992
E-mail: info@yptenc.org.uk
Website: www.yptenc.org.uk

INDEX

ACKNOWLEDGEMENTS

The publisher is grateful for permission to reproduce the following material.

While every care has been taken to trace and acknowledge copyright, the publisher tenders its apology for any accidental infringement or where copyright has proved untraceable. The publisher would be pleased to come to a suitable arrangement in any such case with the rightful owner.

Chapter One: Climate Change

Background information on climate change, © Climate Action Network Europe, *Climate change*, © United Utilities, *The greenhouse effect*, © United Nations Framework Convention on Climate Change (UNFCCC), *Global warming*, © Young People's Trust for the Environment, *Climate change*, © Natural Environment Research Council, *Surface temperatures*, © Crown copyright is reproduced with the permission of Her Majesty's Stationery Office, *Feeling the heat*, © United Nations Framework Convention on Climate Change (UNFCCC), *Global warming clock ticks faster*, © Telegraph Group Limited, London 2004.

Chapter Two: The Effects

How does climate change affect me?, © Worldwatch Institute, *How much climate change can we bear?*, © Greenpeace, *Emissions of carbon dioxide: EU comparison*, © Crown copyright is reproduced with the permission of Her Majesty's Stationery Office, *The impact of climate change*, © People & Planet, *We are all losers in the greenhouse world*, © Friends of the Earth, *Abrupt climate change*, © Friends of the Earth, *Where do CO_2 emissions come from?*, © Friends of the Earth, *Climate change heralds thirsty times ahead*, © Reed Business Information Ltd, *Endangered species*, © NFU Countryside, *Warmer weather, death, disease and destruction*, © CHGL 2004, *Global warming 'will leave Arctic ice-free'*, © Guardian Newspapers Limited 2004, *Climate change and Europe*, © European Environment Agency, *2050: a fictional vision of the future*, © Energy Saving Trust.

Chapter Three: Solutions

The way forward, © WWF-UK, *Climate change: the human factor*, © Energy Saving Trust, *CO_2 emissions by end user, 2002*, © Energy Saving Trust, *Take the climate challenge and save energy*, © Friends of the Earth, *And yet it melts*, © Guardian Newspapers Limited 2004, *Reducing greenhouse gas emissions*, © United Nations Framework Convention on Climate Change (UNFCCC), *Climate change 'to reverse human progress'*, © Guardian Newspapers Limited 2004, *Delivering change*, © United Nations Environment Programme (UNEP), *Renewable electricity*, © Crown copyright is reproduced with the permission of Her Majesty's Stationery Office, *The international fight against climate change*, © Friends of the Earth, *Global warming's uphill challenge*, © Crown copyright is reproduced with the permission of Her Majesty's Stationery Office, *Kyoto saved: not yet the planet*, © Greenpeace.

Photographs and illustrations:

Pages 1, 34: Pumpkin House; pages 4, 16, 31: Don Hatcher; pages 9, 28: Bev Aisbett; pages 11, 23, 33, 39: Simon Kneebone; pages 14, 24: Angelo Madrid.

Craig Donnellan
Cambridge
January, 2005